MATHEMATICAL TOPICS

Introduction to Matrices

MATHEMATICAL TOPICS

Titles in this series will include:

Introduction to Matrices

A. E. Coulson, A.R.C.Sc., B.Sc.,

HEAD OF THE MATHEMATICS DEPARTMENT
GRAMMAR SCHOOL FOR BOYS, DOVER.

Longmans

LONGMANS, GREEN & CO LTD
48 Grosvenor Street, London W1
Associated companies, branches and representatives throughout the world

© A. E. Coulson 1965
First published 1965

Set in Monophoto Times New Roman
by J. W. Arrowsmith Ltd., Bristol 3

Contents

Contents

vi

Section I
Introduction

The development of mathematics in the nineteenth century was so extensive that few mathematicians after Gauss could hope to understand more than a small sector of the subject. Outstanding in the mid nineteenth century was the development of different algebras. For centuries algebra had been applied to numbers: Descartes and Newton had developed the algebra of points represented by numbers; but matrix algebra is the algebra of coefficients of linear equations, such linear equations representing operations or transformations.

Most of the symbols used in matrix algebra are the same as those used in number algebra, but the operations they represent are different or the quantities represented are not the simple numbers of common usage. Before proceeding to the explanation of what matrices are and before defining the symbols used, it is necessary to be clear about the fundamental laws of number algebra.

In the primary school the child learns from handling number apparatus that $3+4$ is the same as $4+3$ and that the order of addition is not important: the result is the same whichever way he does the problem. The numbers 3 and 4 can change places, i.e. COMMUTE (think of the American use of the word *commuter* for a worker who changes places night and morning between his place of work and place of living). We say, in addition of numbers, that the addition is COMMUTATIVE. Similarly the child soon learns that 3×4 is the same as 4×3, i.e. multiplication of numbers is commutative also. When handling three numbers such as 2, 3 and 5, the addition of 5 to the sum of 2 and 3 gives the same result as the addition of 2 to the sum of 3 and 5, that is $(2+3)+5 = 2+(3+5)$. Note that the brackets used in this last expression denote the order of the operations. If we examine the statement $(2+3)+5 = 2+(3+5)$ we see that the 3 can be ASSOCIATED with the 2 first or with the 5, but the sum is obviously the same. In the same way $(2 \times 3) = 6$ and $6 \times 5 = 30$ or $(3 \times 5) = 15$ and $15 \times 2 = 30$, therefore the 3 can be associated with the 2 first or the 5 first and the continued product of $2.3.5$ is still 30: the order of multiplication of numbers is not important. We say that addition and

1

multiplication are ASSOCIATIVE when we are dealing with the algebra of numbers, i.e. $(2 \times 3) \times 5 = 2 \times (3 \times 5)$.

These relations can be expressed using symbols to represent numbers:

I Commutative Laws

(i) For addition
$$a+b = b+a$$

(ii) For multiplication
$$a.b = b.a.$$

II Associative Laws

(i) For addition
$$(a+b)+c = a+(b+c)$$

(ii) For multiplication
$$(a.b)c = a(b.c)$$

By using simple numbers we can illustrate the third important law called the Distributive Law.

III Distributive Laws

(i) $a(b+c) = ab+ac$
(ii) $(b+c)a = ba+ca$

In number algebra the operations involving unit number 1 and zero 0 are important. Early in his number work the pupil learns that a number when multiplied by 1 remains unaltered in value and if zero is added to any number it again remains unaltered. For any number represented by a,

$$a+0 = a$$

and

$$a.1 = a$$

Later he learns that if -2 is added to $+2$ the sum is zero, or if -3 is added to $+3$ the sum is zero, generally $a+(-a) = 0$. Then when he encounters the simple equation $x+a = 0$ he knows that $x = -a$ because $(-a)+a = 0$, but since addition is commutative this is generally written

$$a+(-a) = 0.$$

In multiplication a further difficulty is soon met, when he tries to solve the equation $x.a = 1$ he finds that a cannot be equal to 0. Provided a is not equal to zero, then x is called the RECIPROCAL of a and is denoted by a^{-1}, therefore $a.a^{-1} = 1$.

The process of subtraction in number algebra can be approached in two ways. Thus, directly, we can say '7 minus 3 is equal to 4', i.e. $7-3 = 4$, but this could be turned into a process of addition by asking 'what number added to 3 gives 7', i.e. $7 = 3 + 4$. Generally if $a - b = c$ we say that c is the remainder but then $a = b + c$ and c is the number which must be added to b to give a. The process of division can also be dealt with indirectly as soon as the meaning of the *reciprocal* is appreciated. Thus $3 \div 2$ can be written $\frac{3}{2} = 3 \times \frac{1}{2} = 3 \times 2^{-1}$, i.e. division has become a process of multiplication. Generally for any number a divided by b the result can be obtained by multiplying the number a by the reciprocal of b, i.e.

$$a \div b = a \times \frac{1}{b} = a \times b^{-1}.$$

The algebra of numbers can be reduced to two fundamental operations of addition $(+)$ and multiplication $(\times)$ or $(.)$.

These ideas will be used in matrix algebra and where the symbols of number algebra are appropriate, they will be used in matrix algebra, but often with extended meanings.

Matrix algebra can be approached in different ways, for the pure mathematician it can be started as an abstract algebra of groups or sets of coefficients, but for future scientists, engineers or technologists a more practical approach is often more rewarding and meaningful: such approaches can be started in studying simple electrical theory or elementary equations or linear equations, but all these different approaches lead ultimately in the same direction. With younger pupils methods of CODING messages using matrices are often an exciting way of introducing matrices.

Section II

(2 × 2) Matrices

We start with a study of (2 × 2) matrices in some depth. Many courses on matrix algebra plunge the student into great difficulties before he is familiar with the terms, concepts and processes: frequently the study of (2 × 2) matrices is brief, or neglected, or ignored, whereas it can provide the student with a rewarding introduction to some of the main ideas of matrix algebra and indeed the applications and study of more complicated matrices are only extensions of the applications and ideas which can be acquired so easily by dealing with elementary (2 × 2) forms. In a simple way the student can gain insight into the STRUCTURE of a new algebra of wide application and receive an introduction to many new concepts such as vectors. Any modern course of mathematics must deal with SET theory and MATRIX algebra as its two main branches.

The main practical applications of matrix algebra to linear programming, quantum theory, the theory of relativity, nuclear physics and above all to electrical network theory readily suggest some such practical approach to the subject.

Meaning of a Matrix

Consider the following arrangement.

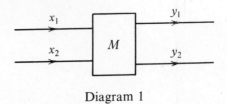

Diagram 1

Suppose M represents an electrical network with x_1 and x_2 representing the inputs to the circuit and y_1 and y_2 the outputs from that circuit which is so constructed that y_1 and y_2 are each dependent on both x_1 and x_2 in a linear fashion. Such circuits can be constructed: this is the sort of condition that arises frequently in electronics. x_1 and x_2 can represent the e.m.f. applied to M or the currents flowing into M, similarly y_1 and y_2 then represent the e.m.f. or currents from the circuit in M. If y_1 depends on both x_1 and x_2 in linear fashion this can be expressed mathematically as

$$y_1 = a_1 x_1 + b_1 x_2 \qquad \text{where } a_1, b_1 \text{ are coefficients, i.e. numbers;}$$

similarly

$$y_2 = a_2 x_1 + b_2 x_2 \qquad \text{where } a_2, b_2 \text{ are coefficients, i.e. numbers}$$

These are linear equations of normal number algebra, on the left-hand side we have the outputs expressed as some operation on the inputs. Using a new notation we can express the relations differently in such a way that the *two* linear equations can be expressed in *one* matrix equation. If the two outputs y_1 and y_2 are put together $\begin{bmatrix} y_1 \\ y_2 \end{bmatrix}$ where the brackets have a special meaning in matrix algebra, then the coefficients a_1, b_1 and a_2, b_2 can be shown similarly as $\begin{bmatrix} a_1 & b_1 \\ a_2 & b_2 \end{bmatrix}$ and the inputs x_1 and x_2 are put together in these special matrix brackets $\begin{bmatrix} x_1 \\ x_2 \end{bmatrix}$.

Now the *operation* which transforms the inputs $\begin{bmatrix} x_1 \\ x_2 \end{bmatrix}$ into the outputs $\begin{bmatrix} y_1 \\ y_2 \end{bmatrix}$ is represented by the matrix $\begin{bmatrix} a_1 & b_1 \\ a_2 & b_2 \end{bmatrix}$, the numbers a_1, b_1, a_2, b_2 are called the ELEMENTS of the matrix.

$\begin{bmatrix} x_1 \\ x_2 \end{bmatrix}$ and $\begin{bmatrix} y_1 \\ y_2 \end{bmatrix}$ are called COLUMN VECTORS or COLUMN MATRICES.

The reason for the alternative use of *column vector* will be given later.

The idea of representing the group of numbers in the correct order, which are responsible for transforming the inputs $\begin{bmatrix} x_1 \\ x_2 \end{bmatrix}$ into the outputs $\begin{bmatrix} y_1 \\ y_2 \end{bmatrix}$ in a MATRIX form was due to CAYLEY in the middle of last century. The numbers in the matrix are the co-efficients of x_1 and x_2 in their correct order—they are ORDERED,

5

DETACHED COEFFICIENTS which have an algebra of their own called *matrix algebra*.

Since this matrix $\begin{bmatrix} a_1 & b_1 \\ a_2 & b_2 \end{bmatrix}$ has two rows and two columns it is called a (2×2) matrix. In words—'a two by two' matrix. If this particular matrix is denoted by capital A and the two column matrices $\begin{bmatrix} x_1 \\ x_2 \end{bmatrix}$, $\begin{bmatrix} y_1 \\ y_2 \end{bmatrix}$ by X and Y, then the operation of the electrical network can now be expressed in this new notation as

$$Y = A.X$$

where A represents an ORDERED set of numbers not *one* number and the product of matrix A with column matrix X must not be mistaken for ordinary multiplication, but a new kind of matrix multiplication (to be investigated later) which yields

$$a_1.x_1 + b_1.x_2$$

and

$$a_2.x_1 + b_2.x_2$$

Before dealing further with matrix multiplication, the process of addition and subtraction of (2×2) matrices will be explained or defined. Many processes are defined, not proved, the definitions giving required results.

In future A will represent a matrix and the small letter a will represent a number in number algebra.

Addition and Subtraction of Matrices

Returning to the original electrical circuit:

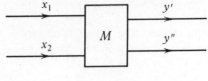

Diagram 2

Suppose that the circuit M is adjusted so that with the original inputs x_1 and x_2, the outputs are now y' and y'' such that

$$y' = a_1 x_1 + b_1 x_2$$

and

$$y'' = a_2 x_1 + b_2 x_2$$

In matrix notation $\begin{bmatrix} y' \\ y'' \end{bmatrix} = \begin{bmatrix} a_1 & b_1 \\ a_2 & b_2 \end{bmatrix} \begin{bmatrix} x_1 \\ x_2 \end{bmatrix}$ or $Y' = AX$.

Now suppose that the circuit M is altered so that an *additional* output y'_α and y''_β is secured in the output channels such that

$$y'_\alpha = a_3 . x_1 + b_3 . x_2$$

$$y''_\beta = a_4 . x_1 + b_4 . x_2$$

In matrix notation $\begin{bmatrix} y'_\alpha \\ y''_\beta \end{bmatrix} = \begin{bmatrix} a_3 & b_3 \\ a_4 & b_4 \end{bmatrix} \begin{bmatrix} x_1 \\ x_2 \end{bmatrix}$ or $Y'' = BX$.

If the *new total outputs* are denoted by y_1 and y_2 as in diagram 1, then

$$y_1 = y' + y'_\alpha \qquad \text{and} \qquad y_2 = y'' + y''_\beta$$

$$\left.\begin{aligned}
y_1 = y' + y'_\alpha &= a_1 . x_1 + b_1 . x_2 + a_3 x_1 + b_3 . x_2 \\
&= (a_1 + a_3) x_1 + (b_1 + b_3) x_2 \\
y_2 = y'' + y''_\beta &= a_2 . x_1 + b_2 . x_2 + a_4 . x_1 + b_4 . x_2 \\
&= (a_2 + a_4) x_1 + (b_2 + b_4) x_2
\end{aligned}\right\} \quad \ldots (1)$$

Using the matrix notation to represent this same addition

$$\begin{bmatrix} y_1 \\ y_2 \end{bmatrix} = \begin{bmatrix} y' \\ y'' \end{bmatrix} + \begin{bmatrix} y'_\alpha \\ y''_\beta \end{bmatrix} = \begin{bmatrix} a_1 & b_1 \\ a_2 & b_2 \end{bmatrix} \begin{bmatrix} x_1 \\ x_2 \end{bmatrix} + \begin{bmatrix} a_3 & b_3 \\ a_4 & b_4 \end{bmatrix} \begin{bmatrix} x_1 \\ x_2 \end{bmatrix} \quad \ldots (2)$$

But in the equations (1) above we have shown that the addition of the outputs can be expressed in matrix form as

$$\begin{bmatrix} y_1 \\ y_2 \end{bmatrix} = \begin{bmatrix} (a_1 + a_3) & (b_1 + b_3) \\ (a_2 + a_4) & (b_2 + b_4) \end{bmatrix} \begin{bmatrix} x_1 \\ x_2 \end{bmatrix} \quad \ldots (3)$$

The matrix relations shown at (2) can be expressed

$$Y = Y' + Y''$$

$$= A . X + B . X$$

$$= (A + B)X$$

from the relations (3).

7

We have demonstrated that the addition of matrices is carried out by the addition of corresponding elements of the matrices in the correct order and all matrix addition is defined in this way.

We have also established for matrix algebra that

$$A.X + B.X = (A+B)X$$

where the curved brackets have the same meaning as in number algebra.

If the circuit M is adjusted so that instead of additional outputs being obtained there is a reduction of outputs y'_α and y''_β then

$$\begin{bmatrix} y_1 \\ y_2 \end{bmatrix} = \begin{bmatrix} y' \\ y'' \end{bmatrix} - \begin{bmatrix} y'_\alpha \\ y''_\beta \end{bmatrix} = AX - BX$$

$$= \begin{bmatrix} a_1 & b_1 \\ a_2 & b_2 \end{bmatrix} \begin{bmatrix} x_1 \\ x_2 \end{bmatrix} - \begin{bmatrix} a_3 & b_3 \\ a_4 & b_4 \end{bmatrix} \begin{bmatrix} x_1 \\ x_2 \end{bmatrix}$$

$$= \begin{bmatrix} (a_1 - a_3) & (b_1 - b_3) \\ (a_2 - a_4) & (b_2 - b_4) \end{bmatrix} \begin{bmatrix} x_1 \\ x_2 \end{bmatrix} = (A - B)X.$$

Subtraction of matrices is carried out by subtracting the corresponding elements of the second matrix from the elements of the first matrix in the correct order.

If $A - B = 0$ we say that the matrices A and B are equal: the elements of matrix B must be equal to the corresponding elements of matrix A for this to be true. This statement is the definition of equal (2×2) matrices.

Examples I

1 Express the following sets of linear equations in matrix notations:

(i) $y_1 = 2x_1 + 3x_2$
$y_2 = 4x_1 + 2x_2$

(ii) $y_1 = 10x_1 + 12x_2$
$y_2 = 25x_1 + 16x_2$

(iii) $x' = 3x + 2y$
$y' = 2x + 3y$

(iv) $x' = 4x - 3y$
$y' = 2x - y$

2 Rewrite the following matrix equations as linear equations:

(i) $\begin{bmatrix} x' \\ y' \end{bmatrix} = \begin{bmatrix} 2 & 1 \\ 4 & 6 \end{bmatrix} \begin{bmatrix} x \\ y \end{bmatrix}$

(ii) $\begin{bmatrix} x' \\ y' \end{bmatrix} = \begin{bmatrix} 3 & 1 \\ 0 & 2 \end{bmatrix} \begin{bmatrix} x \\ y \end{bmatrix}$

3 If $A = \begin{bmatrix} 4 & 6 \\ 5 & 7 \end{bmatrix}$ and $B = \begin{bmatrix} 2 & 3 \\ 1 & 4 \end{bmatrix}$, find matrices C and D such that $C = A + B$ and $D = A - B$.

4 Find with the values of question 3, $B + A$ and compare with $A + B$.

5 If $P = \begin{bmatrix} 2 & 3 \\ 1 & 6 \end{bmatrix}$, $Q = \begin{bmatrix} 1 & 2 \\ 3 & 4 \end{bmatrix}$, and $R = \begin{bmatrix} 1 & 2 \\ 3 & 1 \end{bmatrix}$, find $(P + Q)$, $(Q + R)$, $(P + Q) + R$, $P + (Q + R)$.

6 With the values of P and Q in question 5, find also $Q + P$, $R + Q$ and compare with $P + Q$ and $Q + R$.

7 Using the matrices P, Q and R of question 5, find $(P - Q)$, $(Q - R)$, $(P - Q) - R$, $P - (Q - R)$, and $(P - Q) + R$.

Multiplication of Matrices

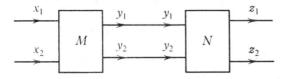

Diagram 3

Now consider an extension to the circuit of diagram 1, so that the outputs from network M are fed into N, i.e. become the inputs to another electrical circuit N, different from M, from which the outputs are z_1 and z_2. Then as on page 5

$$y_1 = a_1.x_1 + b_1.x_2$$
$$y_2 = a_2.x_1 + b_2.x_2$$

i.e. $Y = A.X$ with matrix notation. But the outputs from circuit M become the inputs for circuit N, so that in a similar manner we can state for circuit N

$$z_1 = c_1.y_1 + d_1.y_2$$
$$z_2 = c_2.y_1 + d_2.y_2$$

9

i.e. $Z = B.Y$ where B represents the matrix $\begin{bmatrix} c_1 & d_1 \\ c_2 & d_2 \end{bmatrix}$. For circuit N the outputs $\begin{bmatrix} z_1 \\ z_2 \end{bmatrix}$ are the result of the operation of the coefficients $\begin{bmatrix} c_1 & d_1 \\ c_2 & d_2 \end{bmatrix}$ on the inputs $\begin{bmatrix} y_1 \\ y_2 \end{bmatrix}$ which in turn are the result of the operation of the matrix $\begin{bmatrix} a_1 & b_1 \\ a_2 & b_2 \end{bmatrix}$ on the inputs $\begin{bmatrix} x_1 \\ x_2 \end{bmatrix}$.

To summarize

$$Z = BY$$

and

$$Y = AX$$

$$Z = BY = BAX$$

$$\begin{bmatrix} z_1 \\ z_2 \end{bmatrix} = \begin{bmatrix} c_1 & d_1 \\ c_2 & d_2 \end{bmatrix} \begin{bmatrix} a_1 & b_1 \\ a_2 & b_2 \end{bmatrix} \begin{bmatrix} x_1 \\ x_2 \end{bmatrix}$$

Note the order of the operations B operates on A, not vice versa. By using number algebra we can find by the method of substitution the relation between z_1, z_2 and x_1, x_2 and hence find a meaning for matrix multiplication as follows.

$$z_1 = c_1.y_1 + d_1.y_2 \quad \text{and} \quad y_1 = a_1.x_1 + b_1.x_2$$
$$z_2 = c_2.y_1 + d_2.y_2 \qquad\qquad y_2 = a_2.x_1 + b_2.x_2$$

By direct substitution for y_1 and y_2 in the first set of linear equations

$$\begin{cases} z_1 = c_1(a_1.x_1 + b_1.x_2) + d_1(a_2.x_1 + b_2.x_2) \\ z_2 = c_2(a_1.x_1 + b_1.x_2) + d_2(a_2.x_1 + b_2.x_2) \end{cases}$$

$$\begin{cases} z_1 = c_1.a_1.x_1 + c_1.b_1.x_2 + d_1.a_2.x_1 + d_1.b_2.x_2 \\ z_2 = c_2.a_1.x_1 + c_2.b_1.x_2 + d_2.a_2.x_1 + d_2.b_2.x_2 \end{cases}$$

$$\begin{cases} z_1 = (c_1.a_1 + d_1.a_2)x_1 + (c_1.b_1 + d_1.b_2)x_2 \\ z_2 = (c_2.a_1 + d_2.a_2)x_1 + (c_2.b_1 + d_2.b_2)x_2 \end{cases}$$

$$\begin{bmatrix} z_1 \\ z_2 \end{bmatrix} = \begin{bmatrix} (c_1 a_1 + d_1 a_2) & (c_1 b_1 + d_1 b_2) \\ (c_2 a_1 + d_2 a_2) & (c_2 b_1 + d_2 b_2) \end{bmatrix} \begin{bmatrix} x_1 \\ x_2 \end{bmatrix}$$

i.e.

$$Z = \begin{bmatrix} (c_1.a_1+d_1.a_2) & (c_1.b_1+d_1.b_2) \\ (c_2.a_1+d_2.a_2) & (c_2.b_1+d_2.b_2) \end{bmatrix} X$$

but

$$Z = B.A.X$$

$$\Rightarrow B.A = \begin{bmatrix} (c_1.a_1+d_1.a_2) & (c_1.b_1+d_1.b_2) \\ (c_2.a_1+d_2.a_2) & (c_2.b_1+d_2.b_2) \end{bmatrix}$$

$$\Rightarrow \begin{bmatrix} c_1 & d_1 \\ c_2 & d_2 \end{bmatrix} \begin{bmatrix} a_1 & b_1 \\ a_2 & b_2 \end{bmatrix} = \begin{bmatrix} (c_1.a_1+d_1.a_2) & (c_1.b_1+d_1.b_2) \\ (c_2.a_1+d_2.a_2) & (c_2.b_1+d_2.b_2) \end{bmatrix}$$

The elements of the matrices are just numbers and $(c_1.a_1+d_1.a_2)$ is just a number also. Thus the multiplication of two (2×2) matrices results in a single (2×2) matrix and the form of the process is special to matrix algebra. For consistency matrix multiplication of (2×2) matrices is defined in such a way that the process can be extended to bigger matrices later. Inspection of the products above, shows that the elements of a row of the first matrix B are multiplied by the corresponding elements of a column of the second matrix A, these products being summed for a given row and column to form *one* element of the new matrix. If the *first* row of B and the *first* column of A are used, the element formed is in the *first row* and *first column* of $B.A$: if the *first* row of B and the *second column* of A are used, the element so formed is in the *first row* and *second column* of $B.A$. The row and the column position of each element in $B.A$ is thus uniquely determined by the *row of B* and the *column of A* used to form that element.

The process of matrix multiplication is easily demonstrated by diagrams and quickly learnt by simple numerical exercises.

Example

If $B = \begin{bmatrix} 1 & 2 \\ 4 & 3 \end{bmatrix}$ and $A = \begin{bmatrix} 2 & 3 \\ 3 & 4 \end{bmatrix}$

$B.A = \begin{bmatrix} \boxed{1 \quad 2} \\ \boxed{4 \quad 3} \end{bmatrix} \begin{bmatrix} \boxed{2} & \boxed{3} \\ \boxed{3} & \boxed{4} \end{bmatrix}$ The 1st row of B is $\boxed{1 \quad 2}$

The 2nd row of B is $\boxed{4 \quad 3}$

11

The 1st column of A is $\begin{bmatrix} 2 \\ 3 \end{bmatrix}$

The 2nd column of A is $\begin{bmatrix} 3 \\ 4 \end{bmatrix}$

$$= \begin{bmatrix} \boxed{1 \;\; 2}\,\boxed{\begin{smallmatrix}2\\3\end{smallmatrix}} & \boxed{1 \;\; 2}\,\boxed{\begin{smallmatrix}3\\4\end{smallmatrix}} \\[2mm] \boxed{4 \;\; 3}\,\boxed{\begin{smallmatrix}2\\3\end{smallmatrix}} & \boxed{4 \;\; 3}\,\boxed{\begin{smallmatrix}3\\4\end{smallmatrix}} \end{bmatrix}$$

$$= \begin{bmatrix} \boxed{\begin{smallmatrix}1\\2\end{smallmatrix}} \times \boxed{\begin{smallmatrix}2\\3\end{smallmatrix}} & \boxed{\begin{smallmatrix}1\\2\end{smallmatrix}} \times \boxed{\begin{smallmatrix}3\\4\end{smallmatrix}} \\[2mm] \boxed{\begin{smallmatrix}4\\3\end{smallmatrix}} \times \boxed{\begin{smallmatrix}2\\3\end{smallmatrix}} & \boxed{\begin{smallmatrix}4\\3\end{smallmatrix}} \times \boxed{\begin{smallmatrix}3\\4\end{smallmatrix}} \end{bmatrix}$$

$$= \begin{bmatrix} (1 \times 2)+(2 \times 3) & (1 \times 3)+(2 \times 4) \\ (4 \times 2)+(3 \times 3) & (4 \times 3)+(3 \times 4) \end{bmatrix}$$

$$= \begin{bmatrix} (2+6) & (3+8) \\ (8+9) & (12+12) \end{bmatrix}$$

$$= \begin{bmatrix} 8 & 11 \\ 17 & 24 \end{bmatrix}$$

If we wish to find the product $A.B$ since A is now the first matrix we use the rows of A and the columns of B.

$$A.B = \begin{bmatrix} \boxed{2 \;\; 3} \\ \boxed{3 \;\; 4} \end{bmatrix}\begin{bmatrix} \boxed{\begin{smallmatrix}1\\4\end{smallmatrix}} & \boxed{\begin{smallmatrix}2\\3\end{smallmatrix}} \end{bmatrix}$$

$$= \begin{bmatrix} \boxed{2 \;\; 3}\,\boxed{\begin{smallmatrix}1\\4\end{smallmatrix}} & \boxed{2 \;\; 3}\,\boxed{\begin{smallmatrix}2\\3\end{smallmatrix}} \\[2mm] \boxed{3 \;\; 4}\,\boxed{\begin{smallmatrix}1\\4\end{smallmatrix}} & \boxed{3 \;\; 4}\,\boxed{\begin{smallmatrix}2\\3\end{smallmatrix}} \end{bmatrix}$$

$$= \begin{bmatrix} \boxed{\begin{smallmatrix} 2 \\ 3 \end{smallmatrix}} \times \boxed{\begin{smallmatrix} 1 \\ 4 \end{smallmatrix}} & \boxed{\begin{smallmatrix} 2 \\ 3 \end{smallmatrix}} \times \boxed{\begin{smallmatrix} 2 \\ 3 \end{smallmatrix}} \\[4mm] \boxed{\begin{smallmatrix} 3 \\ 4 \end{smallmatrix}} \times \boxed{\begin{smallmatrix} 1 \\ 4 \end{smallmatrix}} & \boxed{\begin{smallmatrix} 3 \\ 4 \end{smallmatrix}} \times \boxed{\begin{smallmatrix} 2 \\ 3 \end{smallmatrix}} \end{bmatrix}$$

$$= \begin{bmatrix} (2 \times 1)+(3 \times 4) & (2 \times 2)+(3 \times 3) \\ (3 \times 1)+(4 \times 4) & (3 \times 2)+(4 \times 3) \end{bmatrix}$$

$$= \begin{bmatrix} 2+12 & 4+9 \\ 3+16 & 6+12 \end{bmatrix}$$

$$= \begin{bmatrix} 14 & 13 \\ 19 & 18 \end{bmatrix}$$

At once we notice that this result is different from the previous matrix multiplication of $B.A$

$B.A$ is not the same as $A.B$

$$A.B \neq B.A$$

The multiplication of matrices is not commutative in general and this is at once a very distinguishing feature of matrix algebra.

The product $B.A$ is called PRE-MULTIPLICATION of A by B.

The product $A.B$ is called POST-MULTIPLICATION of A by B.

Matrix multiplication can be regarded in another way which has an implication for later work with more complicated matrices.

Again let $A = \begin{bmatrix} 2 & 3 \\ 3 & 4 \end{bmatrix}$ and $B = \begin{bmatrix} 1 & 2 \\ 4 & 3 \end{bmatrix}$.

In matrix A, the elements can be divided into two rows

$$\begin{bmatrix} \boxed{2 \quad 3} \\ \boxed{3 \quad 4} \end{bmatrix}$$ Row 1 R_1 (R suffix 1 denotes Row 1)

Row 2 R_2 (R suffix 2 denotes Row 2)

In matrix B, the elements can be divided into two columns

13

$$\begin{bmatrix} \boxed{\begin{matrix}1\\4\end{matrix}} & \boxed{\begin{matrix}2\\3\end{matrix}} \end{bmatrix},$$

Column 1	Column 2	C_1 denotes column 1
C_1	C_2	C_2 denotes column 2

$$A \cdot B = \begin{bmatrix} \boxed{\begin{matrix}R_1\\ \hline R_2\end{matrix}} \end{bmatrix} \begin{bmatrix} \boxed{C_1} & \boxed{C_2} \end{bmatrix}$$

$$= \begin{bmatrix} R_1 \cdot C_1 & R_1 \cdot C_2 \\ R_2 \cdot C_1 & R_2 \cdot C_2 \end{bmatrix}.$$

In this arrangement the *two suffixes* on each term denote the row and column uniquely.

$$= \begin{bmatrix} \boxed{2\ \ 3}\ \boxed{\begin{matrix}1\\4\end{matrix}} & \boxed{2\ \ 3}\ \boxed{\begin{matrix}2\\3\end{matrix}} \\ \boxed{3\ \ 4}\ \boxed{\begin{matrix}1\\4\end{matrix}} & \boxed{3\ \ 4}\ \boxed{\begin{matrix}2\\3\end{matrix}} \end{bmatrix} = \begin{bmatrix} 14 & 13 \\ 19 & 18 \end{bmatrix}$$

Examples II

1 If $A = \begin{bmatrix} 2 & 3 \\ 1 & 6 \end{bmatrix}$ and $B = \begin{bmatrix} 1 & 2 \\ 3 & 4 \end{bmatrix}$, find $A \cdot B$ and $B \cdot A$.

2 If $P = \begin{bmatrix} 1 & 2 \\ 3 & 1 \end{bmatrix}$ and $Q = \begin{bmatrix} -1 & 2 \\ 2 & -4 \end{bmatrix}$, find $P \cdot Q$ and $Q \cdot P$.

3 If $A = \begin{bmatrix} 2 & 3 \\ 1 & 6 \end{bmatrix}$, $B = \begin{bmatrix} 1 & 2 \\ 3 & 4 \end{bmatrix}$, $P = \begin{bmatrix} 1 & 2 \\ 3 & 1 \end{bmatrix}$, find $A \cdot B$ then

multiply this new matrix by P to find $(A \cdot B)P$: find $B \cdot P$ and then find $A(B \cdot P)$. What do you notice about $(A \cdot B)P$ and $A(B \cdot P)$?

4 With the same values for A, B and P as in question 3, find BA, $(BA)P$, AP and $B(A \cdot P)$. What do you notice about $(BA)P$ and $B(AP)$?

5 Using the same values for A, B and P find $A+B$, $P(A+B)$, $PA+PB$, $B+P$, $A(B+P)$, $AB+AP$. What do you notice about $P(A+B)$ and $PA+PB$, about $A(B+P)$ and $AB+AP$?

6 Why does $(AB)P$ of question 3 differ from $(BA)P$ of question 4?

Scalar Multiplication of a Matrix

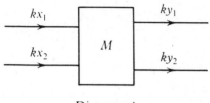

Diagram 4

Returning to the original arrangement of diagram 1, it is obvious that if *both* inputs x_1 and x_2 are increased or magnified by the same number k, then *both* outputs would be altered in the same ratio k, i.e.

$$ky_1 = a_1.kx_1 + b_1kx_2$$

and

$$ky_2 = a_2.kx_1 + b_2kx_2$$

$$k\begin{bmatrix} y_1 \\ y_2 \end{bmatrix} = \begin{bmatrix} a_1.k+b_1.k \\ a_2.k+b_2.k \end{bmatrix}\begin{bmatrix} x_1 \\ x_2 \end{bmatrix} = k\begin{bmatrix} a_1 & b_1 \\ a_2 & b_2 \end{bmatrix}\begin{bmatrix} x_1 \\ x_2 \end{bmatrix}$$

A ratio number such as k is called a SCALAR and the above shows that multiplying a matrix by a scalar means multiplying each element of the matrix by that same scalar.

With ordinary numbers we have shown earlier that division by a number such as 3 is the same process as multiplying by its reciprocal $\frac{1}{3}$. Division of a matrix by a *scalar* number such as 4 is precisely the same as multiplication by the reciprocal of 4, i.e. $\frac{1}{4}$.

However, the division of one matrix by another is *not defined*; the process is avoided by using the reciprocal matrix in multiplication. The reciprocal matrix is now more correctly known as the INVERSE matrix. This process will be developed later.

15

Examples III

1 If $A = \begin{bmatrix} 2 & 3 \\ 1 & 6 \end{bmatrix}$, find $2A, 5A, -3A, kA$.

2 If $B = \begin{bmatrix} 1 & 2 \\ 3 & 4 \end{bmatrix}$, find $4B, kB, -2B$.

3 If $P = \begin{bmatrix} 2 & -1 \\ 3 & -3 \end{bmatrix}$, find $2P, nP, -3P$.

4 Using matrix of question 1, find $A + A$ and compare with $2A$.

The process of subtraction on page 8 can now be considered using the scalar -1.

If $A = \begin{bmatrix} 4 & 7 \\ 3 & 2 \end{bmatrix}$ and $B = \begin{bmatrix} 2 & 3 \\ 4 & 5 \end{bmatrix}$ then $A - B$ can be regarded

as $A + (-B)$ or $A + (-1)B$.

$$A - B = \begin{bmatrix} 4 & 7 \\ 3 & 2 \end{bmatrix} + {}^{-1}\begin{bmatrix} 2 & 3 \\ 4 & 5 \end{bmatrix}$$

$$= \begin{bmatrix} 4 & 7 \\ 3 & 2 \end{bmatrix} + \begin{bmatrix} -2 & -2 \\ -4 & -5 \end{bmatrix}$$

$$= \begin{bmatrix} 2 & 4 \\ -1 & -3 \end{bmatrix}$$

If $A = \begin{bmatrix} 4 & 7 \\ 3 & 2 \end{bmatrix}$ then $A.A = \begin{bmatrix} 4 & 7 \\ 3 & 2 \end{bmatrix}\begin{bmatrix} 4 & 7 \\ 3 & 2 \end{bmatrix} = \begin{bmatrix} 37 & 42 \\ 18 & 25 \end{bmatrix}$.

In matrix algebra $A.A$ is defined as A^2. Similarly $A^3 = A^2.A = A.A.A$.

The Unit Matrix and Zero Matrix

The matrix $\begin{bmatrix} 1 & 0 \\ 0 & 1 \end{bmatrix}$ has special properties.

$$\begin{bmatrix} 2 & 3 \\ 3 & 4 \end{bmatrix}\begin{bmatrix} 1 & 0 \\ 0 & 1 \end{bmatrix} = \begin{bmatrix} (2 \times 1)+(3 \times 0) & (2 \times 0)+(3 \times 1) \\ (3 \times 1)+(4 \times 0) & (3 \times 0)+(4 \times 1) \end{bmatrix}$$

$$= \begin{bmatrix} 2 & 3 \\ 3 & 4 \end{bmatrix}$$

again

$$\begin{bmatrix} 1 & 0 \\ 0 & 1 \end{bmatrix}\begin{bmatrix} 2 & 3 \\ 3 & 4 \end{bmatrix} = \begin{bmatrix} (1 \times 2)+(0 \times 3) & (1 \times 3)+(0 \times 4) \\ (0 \times 2)+(1 \times 3) & (0 \times 3)+(1 \times 4) \end{bmatrix}$$

$$= \begin{bmatrix} 2 & 3 \\ 3 & 4 \end{bmatrix}$$

In both cases the multiplication by $\begin{bmatrix} 1 & 0 \\ 0 & 1 \end{bmatrix}$ has left the original

matrix unaltered. This matrix $\begin{bmatrix} 1 & 0 \\ 0 & 1 \end{bmatrix}$ is called the UNIT MATRIX

because it behaves like the number 1 in ordinary algebra and is denoted by I.

$$A.I = IA = A \quad \text{always.}$$

Similarly it can be demonstrated that the ZERO or NULL MATRIX $0 = \begin{bmatrix} 0 & 0 \\ 0 & 0 \end{bmatrix}$ behaves like the zero of ordinary numbers, i.e.

$$A.0 = 0.A = 0$$

If we consider *any* matrix $\begin{bmatrix} a & b \\ c & d \end{bmatrix}$ pre-multiplication by I and

post-multiplication by I both yield the same result—the original matrix, thus

$$\begin{bmatrix} a & b \\ c & d \end{bmatrix}\begin{bmatrix} 1 & 0 \\ 0 & 1 \end{bmatrix} = \begin{bmatrix} a & b \\ c & d \end{bmatrix} = \begin{bmatrix} 1 & 0 \\ 0 & 1 \end{bmatrix}\begin{bmatrix} a & b \\ c & d \end{bmatrix}$$

It is important to note that this unit multiplication holds for I with *all* other matrices but there are certain matrices where it is possible to find another matrix which will behave in a similar manner, thus let $A = \begin{bmatrix} 2 & 0 \\ -2 & 0 \end{bmatrix}$ and $B = \begin{bmatrix} 1 & 0 \\ 1 & 2 \end{bmatrix}$ then

$$A.B = \begin{bmatrix} 2 & 0 \\ -2 & 0 \end{bmatrix}\begin{bmatrix} 1 & 0 \\ 1 & 2 \end{bmatrix} = \begin{bmatrix} 2 & 0 \\ -2 & 0 \end{bmatrix} = A$$

and

$$B.A = \begin{bmatrix} 1 & 0 \\ 1 & 2 \end{bmatrix}\begin{bmatrix} 2 & 0 \\ -2 & 0 \end{bmatrix} = \begin{bmatrix} 2 & 0 \\ -2 & 0 \end{bmatrix} = A$$

so for these two special matrices

$$AB = B.A = A$$

and matrix B has behaved in this special case like the unit matrix I, but it would not do so with *all* other matrices as I does.

Here follows another peculiarity of matrix algebra—if

$$P = \begin{bmatrix} 1 & -2 \\ 3 & -6 \end{bmatrix} \text{ and } Q = \begin{bmatrix} 4 & 2 \\ 2 & 1 \end{bmatrix} \text{ then}$$

$$P.Q = \begin{bmatrix} 1 & -2 \\ 3 & -6 \end{bmatrix}\begin{bmatrix} 4 & 2 \\ 2 & 1 \end{bmatrix} = \begin{bmatrix} (4-4) & (2-2) \\ (12-12) & (6-6) \end{bmatrix} = \begin{bmatrix} 0 & 0 \\ 0 & 0 \end{bmatrix} = 0$$

Here we have the product of two non-zero matrices being the zero matrix, but

$$Q.P = \begin{bmatrix} 4 & 2 \\ 2 & 1 \end{bmatrix}\begin{bmatrix} 1 & -2 \\ 3 & -6 \end{bmatrix} = \begin{bmatrix} (4+6) & (-8-12) \\ (2+3) & (-4-6) \end{bmatrix} = \begin{bmatrix} 10 & -20 \\ 5 & -10 \end{bmatrix}$$

Hence in matrix algebra if $P.Q = 0$ it does NOT follow that either P or Q is zero, or $Q.P$ has zero value. (Here is another example of the non-commutative property of matrix multiplication $P.Q \neq Q.P$.)

Examples IV

1 If $A = \begin{bmatrix} 2 & 3 \\ 1 & 6 \end{bmatrix}$ and $B = \begin{bmatrix} 1 & 2 \\ 3 & 4 \end{bmatrix}$ and $I = \begin{bmatrix} 1 & 0 \\ 0 & 1 \end{bmatrix}$, verify by matrix multiplication that $AI = IA = A$ and $BI = IB = B$.

2 If $D = \begin{bmatrix} 3 & 4 \\ 1 & 6 \end{bmatrix}$, $E = \begin{bmatrix} a & b \\ c & d \end{bmatrix}$ and $K = \begin{bmatrix} 2 & 0 \\ 0 & 2 \end{bmatrix}$, find DK, KD, KE, EK.

3 If $M = \begin{bmatrix} 2 & 0 \\ -1 & 0 \end{bmatrix}$ and $B = \begin{bmatrix} 1 & 0 \\ 1 & 3 \end{bmatrix}$ and $I = \begin{bmatrix} 1 & 0 \\ 0 & 1 \end{bmatrix}$, find MB, BM, IM, and IB.

4 Using matrices A, B and I of question 1, find

$$A - I, \ A - 3I, \ 2B - I, \ B - kI.$$

5 Using the same matrices, find $(A - B)(A + B)$.

Linear Mappings and Transformations

Transformations using (2 × 2) Matrices

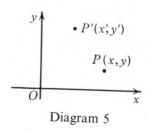

Diagram 5

, If the position of the point P' (co-ordinates x', y') is related to the position of the point P (co-ordinates x, y) by a set of linear algebraic equations thus:

and
$$x' = a_1 . x + b_1 . y$$
$$y' = a_2 . x + b_2 . y \qquad \ldots (1)$$

then we say that P' is a *Linear Mapping* of the point P. For any position of P there is only one possible position of the point P'.

The equations at (1) can be shown in matrix form

$$\begin{bmatrix} x' \\ y' \end{bmatrix} = \begin{bmatrix} a_1 & b_1 \\ a_2 & b_2 \end{bmatrix} \begin{bmatrix} x \\ y \end{bmatrix}$$

and the matrix $\begin{bmatrix} a_1 & b_1 \\ a_2 & b_2 \end{bmatrix}$ represents the operation which transforms the point P to the position P'. We shall consider some of the important transformations and the matrices which cause them.

P' is called the IMAGE of P.

19

Reflection

Consider the transformation $\begin{bmatrix} x' \\ y' \end{bmatrix} = \begin{bmatrix} -1 & 0 \\ 0 & 1 \end{bmatrix} \begin{bmatrix} x \\ y \end{bmatrix}$.

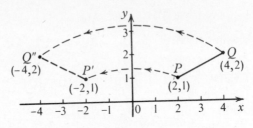

Diagram 6

Apply this transformation to two points $P(2, 1)$ and $Q(4, 2)$ as shown, P becomes

$$P'\begin{bmatrix} x' \\ y' \end{bmatrix} = \begin{bmatrix} -1 & 0 \\ 0 & 1 \end{bmatrix} \begin{bmatrix} 2 \\ 1 \end{bmatrix} = \begin{bmatrix} -2 \\ 1 \end{bmatrix}$$

and Q becomes

$$Q''\begin{bmatrix} x'' \\ y'' \end{bmatrix} = \begin{bmatrix} -1 & 0 \\ 0 & 1 \end{bmatrix} \begin{bmatrix} 4 \\ 2 \end{bmatrix} = \begin{bmatrix} -4 \\ 2 \end{bmatrix}.$$

It is obvious from the linear relations that the points P and Q have been REFLECTED in the y axis to the new positions P' and Q''.

The matrix $\begin{bmatrix} -1 & 0 \\ 0 & 1 \end{bmatrix}$ therefore represents a reflection in the y axis.

From similar considerations, the matrix $\begin{bmatrix} 1 & 0 \\ 0 & -1 \end{bmatrix}$ represents a reflection in the x axis.

In the diagram, P' is the IMAGE of P and Q'' is the image of Q and the transformation is similar to the effect of lateral inversion produced by a plane mirror because we have used *unit values* for the numbers a_1 and b_2.

Stretching

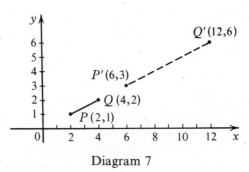

Diagram 7

If the points $P(2, 1)$ and $Q(4, 2)$ are now subjected to the linear mapping $\begin{bmatrix} 3 & 0 \\ 0 & 3 \end{bmatrix}$

then P transforms to

$$P' \begin{bmatrix} x' \\ y' \end{bmatrix} = \begin{bmatrix} 3 & 0 \\ 0 & 3 \end{bmatrix} \begin{bmatrix} 2 \\ 1 \end{bmatrix} = \begin{bmatrix} 6 \\ 3 \end{bmatrix}$$

and Q transforms to

$$Q' \begin{bmatrix} x' \\ y' \end{bmatrix} = \begin{bmatrix} 3 & 0 \\ 0 & 3 \end{bmatrix} \begin{bmatrix} 4 \\ 2 \end{bmatrix} = \begin{bmatrix} 12 \\ 6 \end{bmatrix}$$

The line bounded by P and Q has been *stretched* to the line $P'Q'$ and the plane has been stretched outwards also.

If now we combine the two transformations in a single matrix $\begin{bmatrix} -3 & 0 \\ 0 & 3 \end{bmatrix}$ this will cause both a *reflection* in the y axis and a *stretch* at the same time.

The 'Shear' Transformation

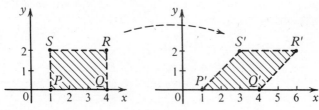

Diagram 8

21

Consider the four points $P(1, 0)$, $Q(4, 0)$, $R(4, 2)$, $S(1, 2)$ and apply the transformation $\begin{bmatrix} 1 & 1 \\ 0 & 1 \end{bmatrix}$ to each $\begin{bmatrix} x' \\ y' \end{bmatrix} = \begin{bmatrix} 1 & 1 \\ 0 & 1 \end{bmatrix} \begin{bmatrix} x \\ y \end{bmatrix}$ or

$$x' = x + y$$

$$y' = y$$

$P(1, 0)$ transforms to $P'(1, 0)$
$Q(4, 0)$ transforms to $Q'(4, 0)$
$R(4, 2)$ transforms to $R'(6, 2)$
$S(1, 2)$ transforms to $S'(3, 2)$

The original points P, Q, R and S defined a rectangle of area 6 sq units, their images, P', Q', R', S', define a parallelogram of the same altitude but suffering a SHEAR to the positive direction. The area of the new figure $P'Q'R'S'$ also has the area 6 sq units. Hence the matrix $\begin{bmatrix} 1 & 1 \\ 0 & 1 \end{bmatrix}$ represents a SHEAR of the plane to the right.

The matrix $\begin{bmatrix} 2 & 3 \\ 0 & 2 \end{bmatrix}$ would have produced both a SHEAR and a stretch of the plane. This is shown in diagram 9.

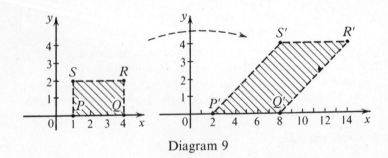

Diagram 9

Again consider the points $P(1, 0)$, $Q(4, 0)$, $R(4, 2)$ and $S(1, 2)$ and apply the transformation $\begin{bmatrix} 2 & 3 \\ 0 & 2 \end{bmatrix}$ to each.

$P(1, 0)$ transforms to $P'(2, 0)$
$Q(4, 0)$ transforms to $Q'(8, 0)$
$R(4, 2)$ transforms to $R'(14, 4)$
$S(1, 2)$ transforms to $S'(8, 4)$

The original points defined a rectangle of area 6 sq units their images now define a parallelogram $P'Q'R'S'$ of area 24 sq units, which shows a magnification in both linear directions and a SHEAR of the plane also. The ratio of the two areas and the matrix causing it will be dealt with in a later section (page 35).

Rotation of Axes about the Origin

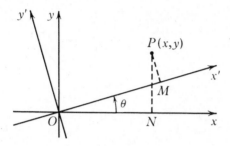

Diagram 10

The point P has co-ordinates x and y with reference to the axes Ox and Oy as shown. PN is the ordinate y and ON the abscissa x. If the axes are rotated through a positive angle θ, to Ox', Oy' then $PM = y'$ in the new axes and $OM = x'$.

It can be shown by trigonometry that

$$x' = \cos\theta.x + \sin\theta.y$$

and

$$y' = -\sin\theta.x + \cos\theta.y$$

i.e. in matrix form

$$\begin{bmatrix} x' \\ y' \end{bmatrix} = \begin{bmatrix} \cos\theta + \sin\theta \\ -\sin\theta + \cos\theta \end{bmatrix} \begin{bmatrix} x \\ y \end{bmatrix}.$$

The matrix $\begin{bmatrix} \cos\theta\sin\theta \\ -\sin\theta\cos\theta \end{bmatrix}$ represents a rotation of the axes

through a positive angle θ. This matrix could also represent a rotation of OP clockwise about the origin, essentially it is a *rotation*. If the angle of rotation is increased to 90° then $\sin\theta$ is equal to 1

23

and $\cos\theta = 0$, the matrix representing a rotation through 90°
becomes $\begin{bmatrix} 0 & 1 \\ -1 & 0 \end{bmatrix}$.

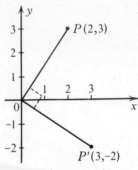

Diagram 11

In diagram 11 the point $P(2, 3)$ is transformed by the matrix $\begin{bmatrix} 0 & 1 \\ -1 & 0 \end{bmatrix}$ to the point $P'(3, -2)$ that is the line OP has been turned clockwise to OP' such that $\lfloor POP' = 1\ Rt.L$. The same transformation would have been obtained if the axes had been rotated anticlockwise through 1 $Rt.L$. Likewise the matrix $\begin{bmatrix} 0 & -1 \\ 1 & 0 \end{bmatrix}$

represents a rotation of OP anticlockwise about the origin O.

We have now shown that multiplication by a matrix represents a transformation so that if this is followed by a second multiplication by another matrix, another transformation follows the first. Now, generally, the ORDER in which transformations are carried out alters the final result. We shall show this geometrically.

Non-commutative Transformations

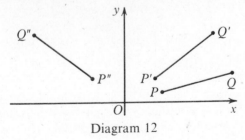

Diagram 12

If the line PQ is rotated through an angle θ to position $P'Q'$ and then reflected in the y axis, we end with $P''Q''$ being the final position. If the reflection is denoted by matrix B and the rotation through angle θ by matrix A, then the operations can be shown algebraically.

$$\begin{bmatrix} x' \\ y' \end{bmatrix} = A \begin{bmatrix} x \\ y \end{bmatrix} \quad \longrightarrow \quad \text{for the rotation}$$

and

$$\begin{bmatrix} x'' \\ y'' \end{bmatrix} = B \begin{bmatrix} x' \\ y' \end{bmatrix} \quad \longrightarrow \quad \text{for reflection}$$

$$\begin{bmatrix} x'' \\ y'' \end{bmatrix} = B.A \begin{bmatrix} x \\ y \end{bmatrix} \qquad A \text{ being pre-multiplied by } B$$

The full transformation of PQ to the final position $P''Q''$ is represented by the product $B.A$ in that order. Now we shall consider the two operations in an alternative order.

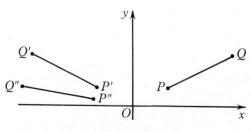

Diagram 13

In this case, if the line PQ is first reflected in the y axis to position $P'Q'$ and then rotated through an angle θ we end with $P''Q''$ being in a different position from diagram 12. Using matrices A and B as before to denote the operations of rotation and reflection in the y axis then the operations can again be shown algebraically:

$$\begin{bmatrix} x' \\ y' \end{bmatrix} = B \begin{bmatrix} x \\ y \end{bmatrix} \qquad \text{for the reflection}$$

and

$$\begin{bmatrix} x'' \\ y'' \end{bmatrix} = A \begin{bmatrix} x' \\ y' \end{bmatrix} \qquad \text{for the rotation}$$

$$\Rightarrow \quad \begin{bmatrix} x'' \\ y'' \end{bmatrix} = A.B \begin{bmatrix} x \\ y \end{bmatrix}$$

But since we have demonstrated that the final result is now different, then $B.A$ is *not* equal to $A.B$. Once more we have shown that matrix multiplication is *not commutative*.

The two processes used in diagrams 12 and 13 can be represented by the two matrices $A = \begin{bmatrix} \cos\theta & -\sin\theta \\ \sin\theta & \cos\theta \end{bmatrix}$ $B = \begin{bmatrix} -1 & 0 \\ 0 & 1 \end{bmatrix}$

then in case I

$$B.A = \begin{bmatrix} -1 & 0 \\ 0 & 1 \end{bmatrix} \begin{bmatrix} \cos\theta & -\sin\theta \\ \sin\theta & \cos\theta \end{bmatrix}$$

$$= \begin{bmatrix} -\cos\theta & \sin\theta \\ \sin\theta & \cos\theta \end{bmatrix}$$

in case II

$$A.B = \begin{bmatrix} \cos\theta & -\sin\theta \\ \sin\theta & \cos\theta \end{bmatrix} \begin{bmatrix} -1 & 0 \\ 0 & 1 \end{bmatrix}$$

$$= \begin{bmatrix} -\cos\theta & -\sin\theta \\ -\sin\theta & \cos\theta \end{bmatrix}$$

and because of the sign changes the results are different, i.e. $B.A$ is not equal to $A.B$ (shown $B.A \neq A.B$).

Examples V

1 A linear mapping is defined by $x' = 2x + 3y$, $y' = 3x + 5y$, give the matrix of this mapping, express the transformation in a matrix equation.

2 If $x' = 3x$ and $y' = y$, express this transformation in matrix form and state what it represents.

3 If $\begin{bmatrix} x' \\ y' \end{bmatrix} = A \begin{bmatrix} x \\ y \end{bmatrix}$ and $A = \begin{bmatrix} -1 & 0 \\ 0 & 1 \end{bmatrix}$, how does this transform the points (2, 3) and (3, 5)?

4 If $\begin{bmatrix} x' \\ y' \end{bmatrix} = \begin{bmatrix} \cos 45° & -\sin 45° \\ \sin 45° & \cos 45° \end{bmatrix} \begin{bmatrix} x \\ y \end{bmatrix}$ and OP is the line joining

the origin $(0, 0)$ to the point $P(2, 3)$, show in a diagram the position of $O'P'$ the image of OP.

5 If $\begin{bmatrix} x' \\ y' \end{bmatrix} = \begin{bmatrix} \dfrac{1}{2} & -\dfrac{\sqrt{3}}{2} \\ \dfrac{\sqrt{3}}{2} & \dfrac{1}{2} \end{bmatrix} \begin{bmatrix} x \\ y \end{bmatrix}$, what is the transformation

produced?

6 If $\begin{bmatrix} x' \\ y' \end{bmatrix} = \begin{bmatrix} \dfrac{1}{\sqrt{2}} & \dfrac{1}{\sqrt{2}} \\ -\dfrac{1}{\sqrt{2}} & \dfrac{1}{\sqrt{2}} \end{bmatrix} \begin{bmatrix} x \\ y \end{bmatrix}$, show in a diagram the position of

$O'P'$ the image of the line OP, joining $(0, 0)$ to $P(2, 3)$. How does this transformation differ from that in question 5?

7 What is the linear mapping produced by the matrix $\begin{bmatrix} 2 & 0 \\ 0 & 2 \end{bmatrix}$?

8 How does the linear mapping of $\begin{bmatrix} 1 & 1 \\ 0 & 1 \end{bmatrix}$ differ from $\begin{bmatrix} 1 & 3 \\ 0 & 1 \end{bmatrix}$?

9 Prove by induction that

$$\begin{bmatrix} \cos \theta & -\sin \theta \\ \sin \theta & \cos \theta \end{bmatrix}^n = \begin{bmatrix} \cos n\theta & -\sin n\theta \\ \sin n\theta & \cos n\theta \end{bmatrix}$$

Trigonometrical Relationships

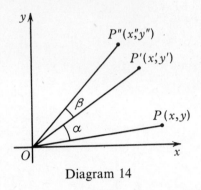

Diagram 14

Let matrix $A = \begin{bmatrix} \cos\alpha & -\sin\alpha \\ \sin\alpha & \cos\alpha \end{bmatrix}$ then the transformation of point
P to P' is represented by A, similarly if $B = \begin{bmatrix} \cos\beta & -\sin\beta \\ \sin\beta & \cos\beta \end{bmatrix}$
then B represents the transformation of P' to P'', therefore the
two rotations which transform OP to $O''P''$ are given by $B.A$,
but the rotation of OP to its final position $O''P''$ means a rotation
through an angle $(\alpha+\beta)$, i.e., $\begin{bmatrix} \cos(\alpha+\beta) & -\sin(\alpha+\beta) \\ \sin(\alpha+\beta) & \cos(\alpha+\beta) \end{bmatrix}$

$$\begin{bmatrix} \cos(\alpha+\beta) & -\sin(\alpha+\beta) \\ \sin(\alpha+\beta) & \cos(\alpha+\beta) \end{bmatrix} = B.A$$

$$= \begin{bmatrix} \cos\beta & -\sin\beta \\ \sin\beta & \cos\beta \end{bmatrix}\begin{bmatrix} \cos\alpha & -\sin\alpha \\ \sin\alpha & \cos\alpha \end{bmatrix}$$

$$= \begin{bmatrix} (\cos\beta\cos\alpha-\sin\beta\sin\alpha) & (-\cos\beta\sin\alpha-\sin\beta\cos\alpha) \\ (\sin\beta\cos\alpha+\cos\beta\sin\alpha) & (-\sin\alpha\sin\beta+\cos\alpha\cos\beta) \end{bmatrix}$$

Equating elements in these two equal matrices we have

$$\cos(\alpha+\beta) = \cos\alpha\cos\beta-\sin\alpha\sin\beta$$
$$\sin(\alpha+\beta) = \sin\alpha\cos\beta+\cos\alpha\sin\beta$$

These two results are of great importance and can be established
in other ways. Most students will meet these formulae in a course

28

of trigonometry, but the matrix method is very straightforward compared with the other methods commonly used and has the advantage over some, that it is general, i.e. applies to angles greater than 90° (if the correct signs are used for sines and cosines).

So far our consideration of matrices has been developed from some *operation* or *transformation* which has been represented by a 2×2 matrix, but having given a practical meaning to a 2×2 matrix such matrices can now be considered as an independent system without continual reference to any operation which they represent.

The Inverse Matrix

Let matrix $A = \begin{bmatrix} 5 & 7 \\ 2 & 3 \end{bmatrix}$ and matrix $B = \begin{bmatrix} 3 & -7 \\ -2 & 5 \end{bmatrix}$. Notice that matrix B has been chosen to have the same numbers for elements but arranged in a different order with some changes of sign

$$A.B = \begin{bmatrix} 5 & 7 \\ 2 & 3 \end{bmatrix}\begin{bmatrix} 3 & -7 \\ -2 & 5 \end{bmatrix} = \begin{bmatrix} 1 & 0 \\ 0 & 1 \end{bmatrix} = I \text{ the unit matrix}$$

again

$$B.A = \begin{bmatrix} 3 & -7 \\ -2 & 5 \end{bmatrix}\begin{bmatrix} 5 & 7 \\ 2 & 3 \end{bmatrix} = \begin{bmatrix} 1 & 0 \\ 0 & 1 \end{bmatrix} = I \text{ the unit matrix.}$$

Multiplication between these two matrices is commutative, i.e. $A.B = B.A = I.$

In number algebra if $a.b = 1$ then $b = \dfrac{1}{a} = a^{-1}$ and we say that b is the reciprocal of a, shown (a^{-1}).

Similarly in matrix algebra, if $A.B = I = B.A$, then B is called the INVERSE MATRIX of A, and is denoted by A^{-1}.

$$A.A^{-1} = A^{-1}.A = I$$

Now take $P = \begin{bmatrix} 5 & 3 \\ 3 & 2 \end{bmatrix}$ and $Q = \begin{bmatrix} 2 & -3 \\ -3 & 5 \end{bmatrix}$

$$P.Q = \begin{bmatrix} 5 & 3 \\ 3 & 2 \end{bmatrix} \begin{bmatrix} 2 & -3 \\ -3 & 5 \end{bmatrix} = \begin{bmatrix} 1 & 0 \\ 0 & 1 \end{bmatrix} = I \quad \text{the unit matrix}$$

$$Q.P = \begin{bmatrix} 2 & -3 \\ -3 & 5 \end{bmatrix} \begin{bmatrix} 5 & 3 \\ 3 & 2 \end{bmatrix} = \begin{bmatrix} 1 & 0 \\ 0 & 1 \end{bmatrix} = I \quad \text{the unit matrix}$$

$$P.Q = Q.P = I$$

Q is the INVERSE of P, i.e. Q is P^{-1}.

In the matrix $P = \begin{bmatrix} 5 & 3 \\ 3 & 2 \end{bmatrix}$ the number 5 is called the *leading element* and a line drawn from 5 in the top left-hand corner to 2 in the bottom right-hand corner is called the *leading diagonal*. A line drawn from the bottom left-hand corner to the top right-hand corner is called the *secondary diagonal*.

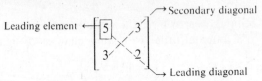

5 and 2 are the elements of the leading diagonal, 3 and 3 are the elements of the secondary diagonal. In each case so far the INVERSE matrix has been formed by *transposing* the elements of the leading diagonal and changing the *signs* of the elements in the secondary diagonal thus

$$\begin{bmatrix} a & b \\ c & d \end{bmatrix} \xrightarrow{\text{INVERSE}} \begin{bmatrix} d & -b \\ -c & a \end{bmatrix}$$

but in each of our examples $(ad - bc)$ has been equal to 1. In matrix P already used $\begin{bmatrix} 5 & 3 \\ 3 & 2 \end{bmatrix}$ $(5 \times 2) - (3 \times 3) = 10 - 9 = 1$.

Now suppose that in the matrix $\begin{bmatrix} a & b \\ c & d \end{bmatrix}$, $(ad - bc) = D$, D not being 0, and we use a method based on the above for finding the Inverse, then providing D is not equal to 0

$$\begin{bmatrix} a & b \\ c & d \end{bmatrix} \begin{bmatrix} d & -b \\ -c & a \end{bmatrix} = \begin{bmatrix} (ad-bc) & (-ab+ab) \\ (cd-cd) & (ad-be) \end{bmatrix}$$

$$= \begin{bmatrix} D & 0 \\ 0 & D \end{bmatrix} = D \begin{bmatrix} 1 & 0 \\ 0 & 1 \end{bmatrix} = D.I$$

Thus, if we now divide each element in the second matrix by this value D we have

$$\begin{bmatrix} a & b \\ c & d \end{bmatrix} \begin{bmatrix} \dfrac{d}{D} & -\dfrac{b}{D} \\ \dfrac{-c}{D} & \dfrac{a}{D} \end{bmatrix} = \begin{bmatrix} \dfrac{ad-bc}{D} & \dfrac{-ab+ab}{D} \\ \dfrac{cd-cd}{D} & \dfrac{ad-bc}{D} \end{bmatrix} = \begin{bmatrix} 1 & 0 \\ 0 & 1 \end{bmatrix} = I$$

Pre-multiplication gives

$$\begin{bmatrix} \dfrac{d}{D} & -\dfrac{b}{D} \\ \dfrac{-c}{D} & \dfrac{a}{D} \end{bmatrix} \begin{bmatrix} a & b \\ c & d \end{bmatrix} = \begin{bmatrix} \dfrac{ad-bc}{D} & \dfrac{bd-bd}{D} \\ \dfrac{-ac+ac}{D} & \dfrac{+ad-bc}{D} \end{bmatrix} = \begin{bmatrix} 1 & 0 \\ 0 & 1 \end{bmatrix} = I$$

Therefore $\begin{bmatrix} \dfrac{d}{D} & \dfrac{-b}{D} \\ \dfrac{-c}{D} & \dfrac{a}{D} \end{bmatrix}$ will always be the INVERSE matrix of

$\begin{bmatrix} a & b \\ c & d \end{bmatrix}$ where $D = (ad-bc)$, providing that $D \neq 0$.

It is more convenient to give $\begin{bmatrix} \dfrac{d}{D} & \dfrac{-b}{D} \\ \dfrac{-c}{D} & \dfrac{a}{D} \end{bmatrix}$ as $\dfrac{1}{D} \begin{bmatrix} d & -b \\ -c & a \end{bmatrix}$

The quantity $(ad-bc)$ is a pure number and is called the DETERMINANT value of the matrix $\begin{bmatrix} a & b \\ c & d \end{bmatrix}$.

The determinant is shown $\begin{vmatrix} a & b \\ c & d \end{vmatrix}$ which is distinguished from the matrix by the use of vertical lines on each side of the group of numbers. In some books the sign $\triangle$ is used to denote the value of the determinant.

If the determinant value of a matrix is zero, the inverse of the matrix does not exist, the matrix is said to be SINGULAR. In the next section the subject of determinant values and singular matrices will be re-examined from a geometrical point of view to give a practical meaning to the determinant, but first two examples of finding an inverse matrix will be presented.

Example (i)

To find the INVERSE of matrix $C = \begin{bmatrix} 2 & 3 \\ 2 & 5 \end{bmatrix}$.

The determinant D is $(2 \times 5) - (2 \times 3) = 4$

$$C^{-1} = \tfrac{1}{4} \begin{bmatrix} 5 & -3 \\ -2 & 2 \end{bmatrix} \quad \text{and} \quad CC^{-1} = \begin{bmatrix} 2 & 3 \\ 2 & 5 \end{bmatrix} \tfrac{1}{4} \begin{bmatrix} 5 & -3 \\ -2 & 2 \end{bmatrix}$$

$$= \tfrac{1}{4} \begin{bmatrix} 4 & 0 \\ 0 & 4 \end{bmatrix} = \begin{bmatrix} 1 & 0 \\ 0 & 1 \end{bmatrix} = I$$

$$C^{-1}.C = \tfrac{1}{4} \begin{bmatrix} 5 & -3 \\ -2 & 2 \end{bmatrix} \begin{bmatrix} 2 & 3 \\ 2 & 5 \end{bmatrix}$$

$$= \tfrac{1}{4} \begin{bmatrix} 4 & 0 \\ 0 & 4 \end{bmatrix} = I$$

$$C.C^{-1} = C^{-1}.C = I$$

Example (ii)

Let $P = \begin{bmatrix} 1 & 2 \\ 3 & 4 \end{bmatrix}$ determinant of $P = 4 - 6 = -2$

$$P^{-1} = -\tfrac{1}{2} \begin{bmatrix} 4 & -2 \\ -3 & 1 \end{bmatrix}$$

$$P^{-1}.P = -\tfrac{1}{2} \begin{bmatrix} 4 & -2 \\ -3 & 1 \end{bmatrix} \begin{bmatrix} 1 & 2 \\ 3 & 4 \end{bmatrix}$$

$$= -\tfrac{1}{2}\begin{bmatrix} -2 & 0 \\ 0 & -2 \end{bmatrix} = \begin{bmatrix} 1 & 0 \\ 0 & 1 \end{bmatrix} = I$$

$$P.P^{-1} = \begin{bmatrix} 1 & 2 \\ 3 & 4 \end{bmatrix}(-\tfrac{1}{2})\begin{bmatrix} 4 & -2 \\ -3 & 1 \end{bmatrix} = (-\tfrac{1}{2})\begin{bmatrix} -2 & 0 \\ 0 & -2 \end{bmatrix} = \begin{bmatrix} 1 & 0 \\ 0 & 1 \end{bmatrix} = I$$

$$P.P^{-1} = P^{-1}.P = I$$

Use of the Inverse Matrix in Coding Methods

Suppose the letters of the alphabet are assigned arbitrary numbers

Table 1

A	B	C	D	E	F	G	H	I	J	K	L	M
1	7	13	11	4	9	16	15	5	24	23	8	22

N	O	P	Q	R	S	T	U	V	W	X	Y	Z
6	2	26	14	10	18	20	3	25	12	17	19	21

Then the word KENT could be coded as 23   4   6   20 and put in a 2×2 matrix as $\begin{bmatrix} 23 & 4 \\ 6 & 20 \end{bmatrix}$.

Let $A = \begin{bmatrix} 23 & 4 \\ 6 & 20 \end{bmatrix}$ and let $P = \begin{bmatrix} 4 & 5 \\ 3 & 4 \end{bmatrix}$ be the coding matrix.

If now A is post-multiplied by P the result will be another (2×2) matrix Q.

$$A.P = Q$$

The word KENT is now coded in the matrix Q with the aid of the coding matrix P, and could be transmitted. At the receiving end, if the inverse of P is known, then

$$Q.P^{-1} = A.P.P^{-1}$$
$$= A(PP^{-1})$$
$$= AI$$
$$= A \quad \text{the original word in number form.}$$

33

$$Q = \begin{bmatrix} 23 & 4 \\ 6 & 20 \end{bmatrix} \begin{bmatrix} 4 & 5 \\ 3 & 4 \end{bmatrix} = \begin{bmatrix} 104 & 131 \\ 84 & 110 \end{bmatrix}$$

The inverse of P is $\begin{bmatrix} 4 & -5 \\ -3 & 4 \end{bmatrix}$ because the determinant is 1.

P^{-1} is the DECODING matrix.

Now $Q.P^{-1} = \begin{bmatrix} 104 & 131 \\ 84 & 110 \end{bmatrix} \begin{bmatrix} 4 & -5 \\ -3 & 4 \end{bmatrix}$

$$= \begin{bmatrix} 23 & 4 \\ 6 & 20 \end{bmatrix}$$

On reference to the original table the letters represented by the numbers give—KENT.

Examples VI

1 Find the determinant of matrix $\begin{bmatrix} 2 & 3 \\ 4 & 5 \end{bmatrix}$.

2 Find the determinant of matrix $\begin{bmatrix} 4 & -6 \\ 2 & 5 \end{bmatrix}$.

3 If $A = \begin{bmatrix} 3 & 2 \\ 3 & 2 \end{bmatrix}$, find $\begin{vmatrix} 3 & 2 \\ 3 & 2 \end{vmatrix}$. What is this class of matrix called?

4 If $A = \begin{bmatrix} 3 & 7 \\ 2 & 5 \end{bmatrix}$, find A^{-1}. Find AA^{-1} and $A^{-1}.A$.

5 Find the product $\begin{bmatrix} 2 & 3 \\ 4 & 5 \end{bmatrix} \begin{bmatrix} 5 & -3 \\ -4 & 2 \end{bmatrix}$. Give the inverse of $\begin{bmatrix} 2 & 3 \\ 4 & 5 \end{bmatrix}$.

6 Using the scheme shown in Table 1, put the word DEAL into a (2×2) matrix and encode using the coding matrix $P = \begin{bmatrix} 5 & 3 \\ 3 & 2 \end{bmatrix}$. Give the decoding matrix P^{-1} and check.

7 Decode the matrix $\begin{bmatrix} 112 & 68 \\ 116 & 74 \end{bmatrix}$ if the coding matrix is $\begin{bmatrix} 5 & 3 \\ 3 & 2 \end{bmatrix}$ and Table 1 was used to number the letters.

8 If matrix $A = \begin{bmatrix} 7 & 4 \\ 2 & 3 \end{bmatrix}$, find A^{-1}.

9 If matrix $P = \begin{bmatrix} p & q \\ v & s \end{bmatrix}$, find P^{-1}.

10 Matrix $Q = \begin{bmatrix} -2 & -5 \\ 3 & 8 \end{bmatrix}$, find Q^{-1}.

11 Find the images P', Q' of the points $P(2, 1)$, $Q(4, 3)$ from the transformation due to the matrix $A = \begin{bmatrix} 3 & 7 \\ 2 & 5 \end{bmatrix}$. Then find the images P'', Q'' of the points P', Q' from the transformation due to matrix A^{-1}. What conclusion do you draw?

12 What transformation is represented by the Inverse of a non-singular matrix?

Geometrical Meaning of the Determinant

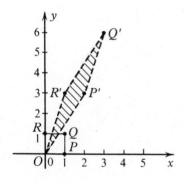

Diagram 15

If O, P, Q, R are the vertices of a unit square O, $(0, 0)$ $P(1, 0)$, $R(0, 1)$, $Q(1, 1)$ and the transformation due to the matrix $\begin{bmatrix} 2 & 1 \\ 3 & 3 \end{bmatrix}$ is carried out then the square $OPQR$ becomes the quadrilateral $OP'Q'R'$ where $O(0, 0)$, $P'(2, 3)$, $Q'(3, 6)$, $R'(1, 3)$ are new vertices as shown. Simple mensuration will show that the AREA of the new quadrilateral is 3 sq. in. and the DETERMINANT of the

35

matrix is also 3. We started with a unit square for convenience, but we could have started with any figure such as a triangle and the *ratio* of the new area to the original area would still be 3 for this matrix. Always the *ratio* in which the area is increased is equal to the *determinant* of the matrix which has been used in the transformation.

The inverse of $\begin{bmatrix} 2 & 1 \\ 3 & 3 \end{bmatrix}$ is $\frac{1}{3} \begin{bmatrix} 3 & -1 \\ -3 & 2 \end{bmatrix}$ or $\begin{bmatrix} 1 & -\frac{1}{3} \\ -1 & \frac{2}{3} \end{bmatrix}$. Now if the points O, P', Q', R' undergo the transformation due to the inverse matrix $\begin{bmatrix} 1 & -\frac{1}{3} \\ -1 & \frac{2}{3} \end{bmatrix}$ *they go back* to the original positions defining a unit square.

The special case of a matrix which is SINGULAR follows.

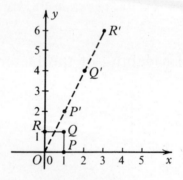

Diagram 16

The matrix $\begin{bmatrix} 2 & 1 \\ 4 & 2 \end{bmatrix}$ is a singular matrix (its determinant is 0 and it will transform the vertices O, P, Q, R of a unit square to points O', P', Q', R' given by

$$x' = 2x + y$$

$$y' = 4x + 2y$$

The point O transforms to $(0, 0)$
The point $P(1, 0)$ transforms to $(2, 4)P'$
The point $Q(1, 1)$ transforms to $(3, 6)Q'$
The point $R(0, 1)$ transforms to $(1, 2)R'$

The unit square has been transformed into a straight line; the quadrilateral $OP'Q'R'$ of figure 15 has now become a straight line (in a sense the singular matrix has produced a quadrilateral of zero area) but the important result is that the original points O, P, Q, R have been transformed to a straight line. This always happens with a 2×2 matrix whose determinant is zero. The idea will arise later with more advanced matrices.

Now the linear mapping represented by $\begin{bmatrix} 2 & 1 \\ 4 & 2 \end{bmatrix}$ is not reversible, this can be shown by trying to solve the equations of the mapping

$$x' = 2x + y$$

$$y' = 4x + 2y$$

to get x and y in terms of x' and y' we have

$$2x + y = x'$$

$$4x + 2y = y'$$

Attempts to eliminate x or y from the left-hand side fail because the determinant $\begin{vmatrix} 2 & 1 \\ 4 & 2 \end{vmatrix}$ is zero.

Whenever the linear mapping is represented by a singular matrix such a mapping is *not* reversible.

In this singular matrix $\begin{bmatrix} 2 & 1 \\ 4 & 2 \end{bmatrix}$ the rows *and* columns have their elements in the same ratio.

The Singular Matrix

Now consider the general (2×2) matrix $\begin{bmatrix} a & b \\ c & d \end{bmatrix}$ and let its determinant be zero, i.e. $ad - bc = 0$.

If

$$ad - bc = 0$$

$$ad = bc$$

$$\frac{a}{b} = \frac{c}{d}$$

Suppose the ratio $\dfrac{a}{b} = k = \dfrac{c}{d}$ then $a = kb$ and $c = kd$. The singular matrix can now be written $\begin{bmatrix} kb & b \\ kd & d \end{bmatrix}$. For any point $P(x, y)$

$$x' = kbx + by = b(kx + y)$$
$$y' = kdx + dy = d(kx + y)$$

For the transform P' of P,

$$\frac{x'}{y'} = \frac{b(kx + y)}{d(kx + y)} = \frac{b}{d} \text{ (constant)}$$

$\Rightarrow$ x' and y' are always in the same ratio and therefore P' will always lie on a straight line.

We have shown that if matrix $\begin{bmatrix} a & b \\ c & d \end{bmatrix}$ is singular then $\dfrac{a}{b} = \dfrac{c}{d}$ which means that the two rows $[a \ b]$ and $[c \ d]$ have their elements in the same ratio and if $\dfrac{a}{b} = \dfrac{c}{d}$ then $\dfrac{a}{c} = \dfrac{b}{d}$ and the elements of the two columns $\begin{bmatrix} a \\ c \end{bmatrix}$ and $\begin{bmatrix} b \\ d \end{bmatrix}$ are also in the same ratio.

It follows that if the elements of the rows, or the elements of the columns, of a matrix are in the same ratio, then the determinant of that matrix is zero. We can show that the product of a *singular* matrix with any other matrix must always result in a *singular* matrix.

For example, let $A = \begin{bmatrix} a & b \\ c & d \end{bmatrix}$ be singular; we have shown that this can be written as $\begin{bmatrix} kb & b \\ kd & d \end{bmatrix}$.

Then if

$$B = \begin{bmatrix} p & q \\ v & s \end{bmatrix}$$

$$A.B = \begin{bmatrix} kb & b \\ kd & d \end{bmatrix} \begin{bmatrix} p & q \\ v & s \end{bmatrix} = \begin{bmatrix} (kbp + bv) & (kbq + bs) \\ (kdp + dv) & (kdq + ds) \end{bmatrix}$$

$$= \begin{bmatrix} b(kp+v) & b(kq+s) \\ d(kp+v) & d(kq+s) \end{bmatrix} = C$$

Since the elements of the rows or columns are in the same ratio therefore C is a singular matrix. Similarly $B.A$ produces another singular matrix.

The INVERSE of a singular matrix is not defined but we are now in a position to examine another use of non-singular matrices in the solution of simultaneous linear equations.

Examples VII

1 If $x' = 4x+5y$, express this transformation in matrix form.

$y' = 2x+3y$

Find the images of the points $O(0, 0)$, $P(1, 0)$, $Q(1, 1)$ and $R(0, 1)$. If $O'P'Q'R'$ is the transformed figure, find its area and compare with the unit square. What is the determinant of the matrix of the transformation? State the relation between the area of the new figure and the determinant.

2 Sketch the quadrilateral $A'B'C'D'$ into which the square $A(1, 0)$, $B(2, 0)$, $C(2, 1)$, $D(1, 1)$ is transformed by the mapping

$$\begin{bmatrix} x' \\ y' \end{bmatrix} = \begin{bmatrix} 3 & 2 \\ 2 & 3 \end{bmatrix} \begin{bmatrix} x \\ y \end{bmatrix}.$$

How does the ratio of the areas $A'B'C'D'$ to $ABCD$ compare with the determinant of the matrix $\begin{bmatrix} 3 & 2 \\ 2 & 3 \end{bmatrix}$?

3 Apply the same transformation $\begin{bmatrix} 3 & 2 \\ 2 & 3 \end{bmatrix}$ to the vertices of the triangle $A(2, 1)$, $B(4, 1)$, $D(3, 3)$. Again find the ratio of the area of $\triangle A'B'C'$ with $\triangle ABC$ and compare with the determinant of the matrix of the transformation.

4 Compare the determinant of $\begin{bmatrix} 2 & 3 \\ 3 & 2 \end{bmatrix}$ with the determinant of $\begin{bmatrix} 3 & 2 \\ 2 & 3 \end{bmatrix}$. Compare the transformations they represent.

5 In question 1 prove that the ratio of the areas is equal to the determinant of the matrix $\begin{bmatrix} 4 & 5 \\ 2 & 3 \end{bmatrix}$.

6 Prove the same result for question 3.

Solution of a Pair of Simultaneous Equations

First if we examine the matrix $\begin{bmatrix} 3 & 4 \\ 2 & 3 \end{bmatrix}$ it is seen that its determinant is $(9-8) = 1$.

Therefore its inverse matrix is $\begin{bmatrix} 3 & -4 \\ -2 & 3 \end{bmatrix}$ and we can apply this to the solution of the pair of simultaneous equations

$$3x + 4y = 18$$

$$2x + 3y = 13$$

These can be written

$$\begin{bmatrix} 3 & 4 \\ 2 & 3 \end{bmatrix} \begin{bmatrix} x \\ y \end{bmatrix} = \begin{bmatrix} 18 \\ 13 \end{bmatrix}$$

$$\Rightarrow \begin{bmatrix} 3 & -4 \\ -2 & 3 \end{bmatrix} \begin{bmatrix} 3 & 4 \\ 2 & 3 \end{bmatrix} \begin{bmatrix} x \\ y \end{bmatrix} = \begin{bmatrix} 3 & -4 \\ -2 & 3 \end{bmatrix} \begin{bmatrix} 18 \\ 13 \end{bmatrix}$$

$$\Rightarrow I \begin{bmatrix} x \\ y \end{bmatrix} = \begin{bmatrix} (\ 54 - 52) \\ (-36 + 39) \end{bmatrix} = \begin{bmatrix} 2 \\ 3 \end{bmatrix}$$

But

$$I \begin{bmatrix} x \\ y \end{bmatrix} = \begin{bmatrix} x \\ y \end{bmatrix}$$

$$\Rightarrow \begin{bmatrix} x \\ y \end{bmatrix} = \begin{bmatrix} 2 \\ 3 \end{bmatrix}$$

For these two column matrices to be the same, their elements must be equal

$$\left. \begin{array}{l} x = 2 \\ y = 3 \end{array} \right\}$$

We would not normally use such a method to deal with a simple pair of simultaneous equations but the method can be extended to any number of simultaneous equations. This will be dealt with later when a general method of inverting any matrix has been developed.

The problem of solving perhaps 100 simultaneous equations in 100 unknowns could arise in connection with industry, technological or scientific research. Using classical methods the problem could require some months of work by one man, but with the aid of a computer and modified method based on matrices, such a problem could be solved in seconds. Much technological progress has been made possible in recent years by the facilities available in computer laboratories.

Examples VIII

1 Restate $2x + 3y = 18$ in matrix form.
$$3x + 5y = 29$$

2 If $\begin{bmatrix} 2-3 \\ 2+3 \end{bmatrix} \begin{bmatrix} x \\ y \end{bmatrix} = \begin{bmatrix} 4 \\ 6 \end{bmatrix}$, multiply the matrices and give the result as a pair of simultaneous equations.

3 If $P = \begin{bmatrix} 2 & 3 \\ 3 & 5 \end{bmatrix}$, $X = \begin{bmatrix} x \\ y \end{bmatrix}$ and $P^{-1} = \begin{bmatrix} 5 & -3 \\ -3 & 2 \end{bmatrix}$, find
$$PX, \ P^{-1}(PX).$$

4 Solve $2x + 3y = 18$ using the matrix method.
$$3x + 5y = 29$$

5 Using the matrix method solve $2x - 3y = 4$.
$$2x + 3y = 6$$

6 Solve the equations $3x - 2y = 5$ by matrix method.
$$8x - 3y = 30$$

7 $A = \begin{bmatrix} 2 & 3 \\ 3 & 4 \end{bmatrix}$, $B = \begin{bmatrix} 1 & 2 \\ 3 & -1 \end{bmatrix}$, $Z = A.Y$ and $Y = B.X$, find matrix C where $Z = CX$. Write down the linear equations which $Z = AY$, $Y = BX$ and $Z = CX$ represent.

41

8 Attempt to solve $3x - 2y = 5$ by the matrix method.
$$6x - 4y = 7$$
Explain why the method fails and sketch the graphs of $3x - 2y = 5$ and $6x - 4y = 7$ on the same pair of axes.

The Transpose Matrix and Orthogonal Matrices

If the rows of a matrix are interchanged with the columns so that the first row becomes the first column and the second row becomes the second column then the new matrix so formed is called the TRANSPOSE of the original.

If $A = \begin{bmatrix} a & b \\ c & d \end{bmatrix}$ then the TRANSPOSE of A (shown) as A' or A^t is

$$A^t = \begin{bmatrix} a & c \\ b & d \end{bmatrix}$$

At once it is seen that the leading diagonal is unchanged and the determinant of the transpose is also unchanged.

Definition

If the matrix A and its transpose A^t have the property that $A . A^t = I$, A is said to be ORTHOGONAL.

It can be shown that the only (2×2) matrices having this property are the matrices of rotation.

Thus if

$$A = \begin{bmatrix} \cos\theta & \sin\theta \\ -\sin\theta & \cos\theta \end{bmatrix} \qquad A^t = \begin{bmatrix} \cos\theta & -\sin\theta \\ \sin\theta & \cos\theta \end{bmatrix}$$

then

$$A . A^t = \begin{bmatrix} \cos\theta & \sin\theta \\ -\sin\theta & \cos\theta \end{bmatrix} \begin{bmatrix} \cos\theta & -\sin\theta \\ \sin\theta & \cos\theta \end{bmatrix} = \begin{bmatrix} (\cos^2\theta + \sin^2\theta) & 0 \\ 0 & (\cos^2\theta + \sin^2\theta) \end{bmatrix}$$

$$= \begin{bmatrix} 1 & 0 \\ 0 & 1 \end{bmatrix} = I$$

but

$$A . A^{-1} = I$$

For an orthogonal matrix $A(2 \times 2)$ the transpose A^t is equal to the inverse matrix A^{-1}.

If matrix A^t is the transpose of matrix A, then it follows that matrix A is the transpose of matrix A^t.

$$(A^t)^t = A$$

Definition

A linear transformation is ORTHOGONAL if it preserves the length of a vector.

The rotation represented by the matrix $\begin{bmatrix} \cos \theta & \sin \theta \\ -\sin \theta & \cos \theta \end{bmatrix}$ certainly preserves the length of the vector as in diagram 11 and is therefore said to be orthogonal. This condition also means that its transpose is equal to its inverse.

Examples IX

1 If $P = \begin{bmatrix} 2 & 5 \\ -2 & 4 \end{bmatrix}$, find P^t (sometimes written P').

2 If $P = \begin{bmatrix} 2 & 3 \\ 3 & 5 \end{bmatrix}$, find P'.

3 If $Q = \begin{bmatrix} \cos \theta & \sin \theta \\ -\sin \theta & \cos \theta \end{bmatrix}$, find Q^{-1} and Q^t.

4 If $R = \begin{bmatrix} \cos x & -\sin x \\ \sin x & \cos x \end{bmatrix}$, find R^{-1} and R^t.

5 To which class of matrices do Q and R belong?

6 $A = \begin{bmatrix} 3 & 4 \\ 2 & 5 \end{bmatrix}$, $B = \begin{bmatrix} 2 & 3 \\ 4 & 7 \end{bmatrix}$, find A' and B'. Find $(AB)'$, $A'B'$ and $B'A'$. State your conclusion.

7 In question 6 compare $|A|$ with $|A'|$ and $|B|$ with $|B'|$.

8 Using matrices A and B of question 6, show that

$$A' + B' = (A + B)'.$$

9 Prove that the only (2×2) matrices which are orthogonal are the matrices of rotation.

Complex Numbers

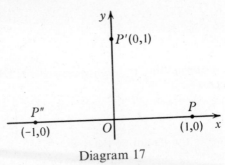

Diagram 17

It was shown earlier that the matrix $\begin{bmatrix} 0 & 1 \\ -1 & 0 \end{bmatrix}$ represents a clockwise rotation through 90°.

If we consider the line OP when point P is $(1, 0)$ then the operation $\begin{bmatrix} 0 & -1 \\ 1 & 0 \end{bmatrix}\begin{bmatrix} 1 \\ 0 \end{bmatrix}$ gives $\begin{bmatrix} x' \\ y' \end{bmatrix}$ the new position P' of P, if the operation is repeated for this new position then the final position of P'' will be $\begin{bmatrix} x'' \\ y'' \end{bmatrix}$ given by

$$\begin{bmatrix} x'' \\ y'' \end{bmatrix} = \begin{bmatrix} 0 & -1 \\ 1 & 0 \end{bmatrix}\begin{bmatrix} 0 & -1 \\ 1 & 0 \end{bmatrix}\begin{bmatrix} 1 \\ 0 \end{bmatrix}$$

$$\begin{bmatrix} x'' \\ y'' \end{bmatrix} = \begin{bmatrix} -1 & 0 \\ 0 & -1 \end{bmatrix}\begin{bmatrix} 1 \\ 0 \end{bmatrix} = \begin{bmatrix} -1 \\ 0 \end{bmatrix}$$

The position $P''(-1, 0)$ shows that the line OP has been rotated *anticlockwise* to OP'' since O is transformed into itself.

But OP is 1 units long and OP' is -1 units long.

$\therefore$ Double transformation $\begin{bmatrix} 0 & -1 \\ 1 & 0 \end{bmatrix}\begin{bmatrix} 0 & -1 \\ 1 & 0 \end{bmatrix}$ alters the sign of

OP from positive to negative.

If we call the matrix $\begin{bmatrix} 0 & -1 \\ 1 & 0 \end{bmatrix}$ R, then the operation R^2 is equivalent to -1. i.e. R is equivalent to $\sqrt{-1}$. But $\sqrt{-1}$ is represented in mathematics by i,

$$\therefore \quad R = \begin{bmatrix} 0 & -1 \\ 1 & 0 \end{bmatrix} \text{ is the matrix form of } i.$$

This could have been demonstrated differently thus:

$$R^2 = R.R = \begin{bmatrix} 0 & -1 \\ 1 & 0 \end{bmatrix}\begin{bmatrix} 0 & -1 \\ 1 & 0 \end{bmatrix} = \begin{bmatrix} -1 & 0 \\ 0 & -1 \end{bmatrix} = (-1)I$$

and again R^2 represents -1, i.e. R represents $\sqrt{-1}$ or i.

Leonard Euler first used the sign i (in 1777) to represent the square root of minus one in order that he could give the solution of the equation $x^2 + 1 = 0$, but the graphical representation of $\sqrt{-1}$ as a rotation through $90°$ was first presented by Caspar Wessel in 1797 in a paper on the subject read to the Royal Academy of Denmark. Other mathematicians of this period, including Gauss, also used the same plan to represent $\sqrt{-1}$ graphically and the treatment by J. R. Argand in 1806 at Paris was so successful that he is remembered most frequently in this work. The ARGAND plane to represent complex numbers is a constant reminder of his contribution.

In his work, Gauss realized that the purely imaginary number $b\sqrt{-1}$ and the number which is partly real and partly imaginary, $a + b\sqrt{-1}$, needed differentiation by name, for the latter kind of number he used the word COMPLEX which has remained in use since.

Note: Since electrical engineers use the symbol i to represent alternating currents they use the symbol j for $\sqrt{-1}$. The difference need not be confusing, in pure mathematics we continue to use i but whenever electrical alternating theory is under treatment i is replaced by j.

The imaginary number $b\sqrt{-1}$ corresponds to the matrix

$$b\begin{bmatrix} 0 & -1 \\ 1 & 0 \end{bmatrix} = \begin{bmatrix} 0 & -b \\ b & 0 \end{bmatrix}.$$

45

The real number a corresponds to the matrix $\begin{bmatrix} a & 0 \\ 0 & a \end{bmatrix}$, i.e. aI, so the complex number $a+bi$ corresponds to the matrix given by

$$aI + b\begin{bmatrix} 0 & -1 \\ 1 & 0 \end{bmatrix} = \begin{bmatrix} a & 0 \\ 0 & a \end{bmatrix} + \begin{bmatrix} 0 & -b \\ b & 0 \end{bmatrix}$$

$$= \begin{bmatrix} a & -b \\ b & a \end{bmatrix}$$

$\begin{bmatrix} a & -b \\ b & a \end{bmatrix}$ is the matrix corresponding to the complex number $a+bi$. The leading diagonal gives the REAL number and the secondary diagonal gives the IMAGINARY number.

The operations carried out with complex numbers correspond exactly to the matrix operations with the matrix form.

Consider addition of $a+bi$ and $c+di$. Adding the real and imaginary parts separately gives

$$(a+bi)+(c+di) = (a+c)+(b+d)i.$$

The corresponding matrix operation produces a similar result

$$\begin{bmatrix} a & -b \\ b & a \end{bmatrix} + \begin{bmatrix} c & -d \\ d & c \end{bmatrix} = \begin{bmatrix} (a+c)-(b+d) \\ (b+d) & (a+c) \end{bmatrix}$$

Again multiplication of the same two numbers corresponds exactly:

$$\begin{bmatrix} a & -b \\ b & a \end{bmatrix}\begin{bmatrix} c & -d \\ d & c \end{bmatrix} = \begin{bmatrix} (ac-bd)-(ad+bc) \\ (bc+ad) & (ac-bd) \end{bmatrix}$$

Real part $ac-bd$, imaginary part $(ad+bd)i$ and

$$(a+bi)(c+di) = ac+i^2bd+(bc+ad)i$$

$$= (ac-bd)+(bc+ad)i \quad \text{since} \quad i^2 = -1.$$

So the group of 2×2 matrices of the form $\begin{bmatrix} a & -b \\ b & a \end{bmatrix}$ gives exactly corresponding forms for addition and multiplication as the group of complex numbers of the form $a+bi$. This exact correspondence between two groups is called ISOMORPHISM and the group of

(2×2) matrices which correspond to the complex numbers is said to be ISOMORPHIC to the group of complex numbers. Many problems in complex numbers can be solved by the use of the corresponding isomorphic forms of matrices. Thus

Example (i)

$$(3+2i)(2+3i) \text{ becomes } \begin{bmatrix} 3 & -2 \\ 2 & 3 \end{bmatrix} \begin{bmatrix} 2 & -3 \\ 3 & 2 \end{bmatrix} = \begin{bmatrix} 0 & -13 \\ 13 & 0 \end{bmatrix}$$

$$= 13 \begin{bmatrix} 0 & -1 \\ 1 & 0 \end{bmatrix}$$

$$\Rightarrow (3+2i)(2+3i) = 13i$$

Example (ii)

To find $\dfrac{3+2i}{2-3i}$.

Since division in matrix algebra is not defined we must multiply by the inverse matrix.

$$\begin{bmatrix} 3 & -2 \\ 2 & 3 \end{bmatrix} \begin{bmatrix} \frac{2}{13} & -\frac{3}{13} \\ \frac{3}{13} & \frac{2}{13} \end{bmatrix} = \begin{bmatrix} 0 & -\frac{13}{13} \\ \frac{13}{13} & 0 \end{bmatrix} = \begin{bmatrix} 0 & -1 \\ 1 & 0 \end{bmatrix} = i$$

The matrices $\begin{bmatrix} a & -b \\ b & a \end{bmatrix}$ where a and b take all real values can be considered as the *mathematical model* of complex numbers.

Examples X

1 Add $2+3i$ and $3+2i$ using matrix form.

2 Subtract $2+3i$ from $6+4i$ using matrix form.

3 Find $(2-3i)(4-5i)$ using matrix form.

4 Find $(2+3i)^2$ using matrix form.

5 $\dfrac{2+3i}{3-2i} = (2+3i)(3-2i)^{-1}$, hence, using the matrix forms, find $\dfrac{2+3i}{3-2i}$.

6 Put $r \cos \theta + r \sin \theta i$ in matrix form, $r \begin{bmatrix} & \\ & \end{bmatrix}$.

7 If $Z_1 = r_1(\cos \theta_1 + i \sin \theta_1)$ and $Z_2 = r_2(\cos \theta_2 + i \sin \theta_2)$, express each of these in matrix form and then find $Z_1 . Z_2$ and simplify.

Vectors

On page 5 single column matrices were called column vectors or column matrices. We are now at a stage when this idea can be expanded further.

The engineer and scientist have long recognized quantities which have *both* magnitude and direction and other quantities which have only magnitude or size. *Quantities having magnitude and direction have been given the name* VECTOR. The name was adopted by Sir W. R. Hamilton about 1853 when he first published a full treatment on Quaternions. Quantities which have magnitude only can be represented by a single number and are called SCALARS.

The engineer has a very clear idea of what he means to be VECTOR quantities, like FORCE, VELOCITY, MOMENTUM, ACCELERATION. The mathematician finds that he can represent vectors in a plane by a pair of ordered numbers, vectors in three dimensional space by a triple of ordered numbers and mathematical quantities which require four or more ordered numbers to specify them are for him an extension of the system of vectors. A mathematical quantity which requires n ordered numbers to specify it completely is called a *vector of n dimensions*.

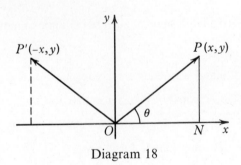

Diagram 18

If OP represents a VECTOR in a plane, the distance OP represents the magnitude and the direction is given by the angle θ and the sense by the arrowhead. The complete direction is given by the two ordered, real numbers (x, y) since $y/x = \tan \theta$ and the sense O to P is determined by the algebraic sign of x, and y. If P' is the point $(-x, y)$ then the new sense is shown, the magnitude remaining constant. By Pythagoras the length $OP = \sqrt{x^2 + y^2}$ shown mod. OP or $|\overrightarrow{OP}|$.

Our earlier use of $\begin{bmatrix} x \\ y \end{bmatrix}$ was in fact then a vector representation in a space of two dimensions, hence the use of the term *column vector*. Now the transpose of $\begin{bmatrix} x \\ y \end{bmatrix}$ is defined as $[x \quad y]$ called a ROW VECTOR.

On page 19 where a linear mapping is explained the transformation which operates on the column vector $\begin{bmatrix} x \\ y \end{bmatrix}$ produces another column vector $\begin{bmatrix} x' \\ y' \end{bmatrix}$ so that in this case the equation in matrix form

$$\begin{bmatrix} x' \\ y' \end{bmatrix} = \begin{bmatrix} a_1 & b_1 \\ a_2 & b_2 \end{bmatrix} \begin{bmatrix} x \\ y \end{bmatrix} \qquad \ldots (1)$$

represents a *vector relation*.

The matrix $\begin{bmatrix} a_1 & b_1 \\ a_2 & b_2 \end{bmatrix}$ can be regarded as the composition of two column vectors or of two row vectors.

In the relation (1) above, the row vector or row matrix $[a_1 \quad b_1]$ operating on the column matrix $\begin{bmatrix} x \\ y \end{bmatrix}$ gives the single equation

$$x' = [a_1 \quad b_1]\begin{bmatrix} x \\ y \end{bmatrix}$$

since

$$x' = a_1 x + b_1 y$$

and

$$y' = [a_2 \quad b_2]\begin{bmatrix} x \\ y \end{bmatrix}$$

i.e.

$$y' = a_2 x + b_2 y$$

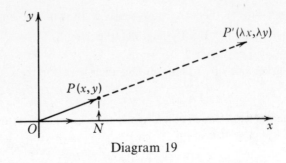

Diagram 19

Let the vector $\overrightarrow{OP}$ be specified by the ordered pair of numbers (x, y). Then the vector $(\lambda x, \lambda y)$ will have the direction of $\overrightarrow{OP}$, but depending on λ, OP' will fall *along OP* and if λ is greater than 1 there will be magnification. If λ is less than 1, there will be compression but mathematically this is still termed magnification. If P' is the point $\lambda x, \lambda y$ then vectors $\overrightarrow{OP}$ and $\overrightarrow{OP'}$ have the *same direction* (or are parallel).

If λ is a negative number the vector $\overrightarrow{OP'}$ will have the same direction but *opposite sense to* $\overrightarrow{OP}$.

The engineer working with *vector quantities* regards the vector $\overrightarrow{OP}$ as the resultant of two displacements $\overrightarrow{ON}$ to the right and $\overrightarrow{NP}$ upwards as shown. All the properties of vectors which the engineer and scientist use are included in the *mathematical model* which the mathematician has built with the system of ordered pairs of numbers, or ordered triples of numbers.

The Addition of two Vectors

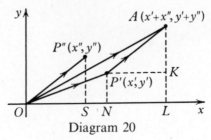

Diagram 20

We use the column matrix $\begin{bmatrix} x \\ y \end{bmatrix}$ to represent a vector. In the diagram OP' and OP'' are two vectors $OP' = \begin{bmatrix} x' \\ y' \end{bmatrix}$ and $OP'' = \begin{bmatrix} x'' \\ y'' \end{bmatrix}$.

$OP' + OP'' = \begin{bmatrix} x' \\ y' \end{bmatrix} + \begin{bmatrix} x'' \\ y'' \end{bmatrix}$ by the method of matrix addition this

becomes

$$= \begin{bmatrix} x' + x'' \\ y' + y'' \end{bmatrix}$$

In the figure, $OL = ON + NL = ON + P'K = x' + x''$

$$AL = AK + KL = y'' + y' = y' + y''$$

The vector $OA = \begin{bmatrix} x' + x'' \\ y' + y'' \end{bmatrix}$ and represents the addition of OP'

and OP''.

This form of addition of two vectors agrees exactly with the form adopted by the engineer and scientist when he is adding *vector quantities*.

Examples XI

1 (i) Show diagrammatically the vectors $\vec{OP}$ and $\vec{OP'}$ where

$$\vec{OP} = \begin{bmatrix} 3 \\ 2 \end{bmatrix} \text{ and } \vec{OP'} = \begin{bmatrix} 1 \\ 4 \end{bmatrix}.$$

(ii) $\vec{OP} + \vec{OP'} = \begin{bmatrix} 3 \\ 2 \end{bmatrix} + \begin{bmatrix} 1 \\ 4 \end{bmatrix} = \begin{matrix} (3+1). \\ (2+4) \end{matrix}$ By addition of column

matrices $= \begin{bmatrix} 4 \\ 6 \end{bmatrix} = OR.$

On your diagram show $\vec{OR}$ the sum of the two vectors $\vec{OP}$ and $\vec{OP'}$.

2 Using the same vectors $OP = \begin{bmatrix} 3 \\ 2 \end{bmatrix} OP' = \begin{bmatrix} 1 \\ 4 \end{bmatrix}$ show

$$\vec{OP} - \vec{OP'} = \vec{OS},$$

where OS is obtained first by subtraction of column matrices.

3 Show the vectors $OA = \begin{bmatrix} 4 \\ 0 \end{bmatrix}$ $OB = \begin{bmatrix} 0 \\ 3 \end{bmatrix}$ and $\vec{OC} = \vec{OA} + \vec{OB}$,

give vector $\vec{OC}$ as a column matrix.

4 Show the vector $\vec{OP} = \begin{bmatrix} 4 \\ 2 \end{bmatrix}$ $OQ = \begin{bmatrix} 2 \\ 5 \end{bmatrix}$ and $\vec{OR} = \vec{OP} + \vec{OQ}$.

Join the points PR and QR. Which kind of quadrilateral is formed by $OPRQ$?

5 Draw a pair of straight lines OA and OB as axes at any acute angle AOB (say 70°). Now show the vectors of question 4. What is the figure $OPRQ$ in this case with oblique axes?

Matrix as a Store of Information

The section on coding methods on page 33 shows that a matrix can also serve as a STORE *of information* classified in numerical form. This illustrates one of the most important uses of matrix methods in linear Programming, Computer Control and in the analysis of many processes such as *Programmed Instruction Studies* and *Psychological Testing*. Four letter words can be stored in a 2×2 matrix by the method shown: processes could be stored in matrix form by a similar coding. Other matrices of a special form can then operate on the stored information. Some of these special matrices are given.

Matrices of special operation

The matrix $\begin{bmatrix} 0 & 1 \\ 1 & 0 \end{bmatrix}$ causes the operation of *reversal* thus

(i) Post-multiplication causes interchange of columns:

$$\begin{bmatrix} a & b \\ c & d \end{bmatrix}\begin{bmatrix} 0 & 1 \\ 1 & 0 \end{bmatrix} = \begin{bmatrix} b & a \\ d & c \end{bmatrix}$$

(ii) Pre-multiplication gives interchange of row:

$$\begin{bmatrix} 0 & 1 \\ 1 & 0 \end{bmatrix}\begin{bmatrix} a & b \\ c & d \end{bmatrix} = \begin{bmatrix} c & d \\ a & b \end{bmatrix}$$

The matrix $\begin{bmatrix} 1 & 1 \\ 0 & 1 \end{bmatrix}$ causes the operation of *addition* thus

(i) Post-multiplication (addition of columns)

$$\begin{bmatrix} a & b \\ c & d \end{bmatrix} \begin{bmatrix} 1 & 1 \\ 0 & 1 \end{bmatrix} = \begin{bmatrix} a & a+b \\ c & c+d \end{bmatrix}$$

(ii) Pre-multiplication (addition of rows)

$$\begin{bmatrix} 1 & 1 \\ 0 & 1 \end{bmatrix} \begin{bmatrix} a & b \\ c & d \end{bmatrix} = \begin{bmatrix} a+c & b+d \\ c & d \end{bmatrix}$$

The matrix $A^t = \begin{bmatrix} 1 & 0 \\ 1 & 1 \end{bmatrix}$ is the TRANSPOSE of the matrix

$$A = \begin{bmatrix} 1 & 1 \\ 0 & 1 \end{bmatrix},$$

i.e. rows and columns have been interchanged.

The transpose $\begin{bmatrix} 1 & 0 \\ 1 & 1 \end{bmatrix}$ also causes addition thus

(i) Post-multiplication $\begin{bmatrix} a & b \\ c & d \end{bmatrix} \begin{bmatrix} 1 & 0 \\ 1 & 1 \end{bmatrix} = \begin{bmatrix} a+b & b \\ c+d & d \end{bmatrix}$

But the addition is now stored in the *first column*.

(ii) Pre-multiplication $\begin{bmatrix} 1 & 0 \\ 1 & 1 \end{bmatrix} \begin{bmatrix} a & b \\ c & d \end{bmatrix} = \begin{bmatrix} a & b \\ a+c & b+d \end{bmatrix}$ shows that

the addition is now stored in the *second row*.

The two matrices $\begin{bmatrix} 1 & 1 \\ 0 & 1 \end{bmatrix}$ and $\begin{bmatrix} 1 & 0 \\ 1 & 1 \end{bmatrix}$ are both examples of

TRIANGULAR matrices having the properties illustrated above. They are called triangular because the elements lie to one side only of one of the diagonals. $\begin{bmatrix} 1 & 1 \\ 0 & 1 \end{bmatrix}$ and $\begin{bmatrix} 1 & 0 \\ 1 & 1 \end{bmatrix}$

These forms will be met again in more complicated forms of matrices.

Elementary Matrices

The types of operations on rows (or columns) such as the addition of rows or reversal of columns or interchange of rows are produced by *elementary matrices*.

The five elementary matrices and their geometrical equivalent interpretation:

I	$\begin{bmatrix} 0 & 1 \\ 1 & 0 \end{bmatrix}$	A reflection of the plane in the line through the origin at 45° to the x axis.
II	$\begin{bmatrix} a & 0 \\ 0 & 1 \end{bmatrix}$	An elongation or compression parallel to the x axis.
III	$\begin{bmatrix} 1 & 0 \\ 0 & a \end{bmatrix}$	An elongation or compression parallel to the y axis.
IV	$\begin{bmatrix} 1 & 0 \\ b & 1 \end{bmatrix}$	A shear parallel to the y axis.
V	$\begin{bmatrix} 1 & b \\ 0 & 1 \end{bmatrix}$	A shear parallel to the x axis.

Any linear transformation of the plane may be represented as a product of reflections, shears and elongations in one dimension.

Nilpotent Matrices

A matrix of the form $\begin{bmatrix} 0 & 2 \\ 0 & 0 \end{bmatrix}$ has special properties also.

If $T = \begin{bmatrix} 0 & 2 \\ 0 & 0 \end{bmatrix}$ then $T.T = \begin{bmatrix} 0 & 2 \\ 0 & 0 \end{bmatrix}\begin{bmatrix} 0 & 2 \\ 0 & 0 \end{bmatrix} = \begin{bmatrix} 0 & 0 \\ 0 & 0 \end{bmatrix}$, the NULL

matrix   i.e. $T^2 = 0$

$$\Rightarrow \quad T^3 = T^2.T = 0.T = 0$$

Thus T is a matrix which has the special property namely that powers of itself are zero.

In number algebra the only number whose square is zero is zero itself.

Here then is another difference between matrix algebra and number algebra. The property of matrices like T will be met again.

Such matrices as T are said to be NILPOTENT.

Examples XII

1   $A = \begin{bmatrix} 3 & 4 \\ -2 & 1 \end{bmatrix}$, $H = \begin{bmatrix} 0 & 1 \\ 1 & 0 \end{bmatrix}$, find AH and HA.

2   $B = \begin{bmatrix} 4 & 3 \\ 2 & -2 \end{bmatrix}$ and $K = \begin{bmatrix} 1 & 3 \\ 0 & 1 \end{bmatrix}$, find KB and BK.

3   $C = \begin{bmatrix} 5 & -2 \\ 1 & 3 \end{bmatrix}$ and $L = \begin{bmatrix} 1 & 0 \\ -2 & 1 \end{bmatrix}$, find LC and CL.

4   $D = \begin{bmatrix} 10 & 2 \\ 3 & -6 \end{bmatrix}$ and $N = \begin{bmatrix} 1 & 0 \\ 0 & 3 \end{bmatrix}$, find DN and ND.

5   $T = \begin{bmatrix} 0 & 3 \\ 0 & 0 \end{bmatrix}$, $A = \begin{bmatrix} 3 & 4 \\ -2 & 1 \end{bmatrix}$, find T^2 and TA and AT.

6   $F = \begin{bmatrix} 0 & 2 \\ 0 & 2 \end{bmatrix}$ and $B = \begin{bmatrix} 4 & 3 \\ 2 & -2 \end{bmatrix}$, find F^2, FB and BF.

7   $P = \begin{bmatrix} a & b \\ c & d \end{bmatrix}$, $A = \begin{bmatrix} -2 & 0 \\ 0 & -2 \end{bmatrix}$, $B = \begin{bmatrix} 0 & 3 \\ 3 & 0 \end{bmatrix}$, find AP, PA, AB, BA, BP, PB.

8   What geometrical transformations are represented by the matrices H, K, L and N above?

Distributive Laws for Scalar Multiplication

Scalar multiplication of matrices will now be extended. We have demonstrated earlier that the multiplication of a matrix by a scalar number k is equivalent to multiplication of each element of the matrix by k.

Let $A = \begin{bmatrix} a_1 & a_2 \\ a_3 & a_4 \end{bmatrix}$ and $B = \begin{bmatrix} b_1 & b_2 \\ b_3 & b_4 \end{bmatrix}$

$kA = \begin{bmatrix} ka_1 & ka_2 \\ ka_3 & ka_4 \end{bmatrix}$ and $kB = \begin{bmatrix} kb_1 & kb_2 \\ kb_3 & kb_4 \end{bmatrix}$

$$kA + kB = \begin{bmatrix} ka_1 & ka_2 \\ ka_3 & ka_4 \end{bmatrix} + \begin{bmatrix} kb_1 & kb_2 \\ kb_3 & kb_4 \end{bmatrix}$$

$$= \begin{bmatrix} ka_1 + kb_1 & ka_2 + kb_2 \\ ka_3 + kb_3 & ka_4 + kb_4 \end{bmatrix}$$

$$= \begin{bmatrix} k(a_1 + b_1) & k(a_2 + b_2) \\ k(a_3 + b_3) & k(a_4 + b_4) \end{bmatrix}$$

$$= k\begin{bmatrix} (a_1 + b_1) & (a_2 + b_2) \\ (a_3 + b_3) & (a_4 + b_4) \end{bmatrix}$$

$$= k(A + B)$$

Similarly it can be shown that $k(A + B) = kA + kB$. These two relations are the Distributive Laws for Scalar Multiplication.

Laws for the Addition and Multiplication of (2×2) Matrices

At this stage it is useful to summarize some of the work done so far. At the beginning we showed by practical situations involving operations or transformations that (2×2) matrices could represent such processes. It later became obvious that (2×2) matrices constitute an independent system with an algebra of its own, similar in many ways to ordinary number algebra, but different in one very important feature that multiplication is *not* commutative. Such a system of (2×2) matrices constitutes a RING. From the examples given the algebra of (2×2) matrices obeys the following laws for addition:

(i) $A + B = B + A$ (Commutative Law for addition)
(ii) $(A + B) + C = A + (B + C)$ (Associative Law for addition)
(iii) $A + O = A$ (Null or Zero matrix is the Identity element for addition)

where the $+$ sign has the special meaning in matrix algebra of adding corresponding elements.

The multiplication of (2×2) matrices follows these laws:

(i) $(AB)C = A(BC)$ (Associative Law for multiplication)

(ii) $(A+B)C = AC+BC$ (Distributive Law for multiplication)

$C(A+B) = CA+CB$ Note the order of multiplication since multiplication is not commutative

(iii) $AI = IA = A$ Unit matrix is the Identity element for multiplication.

Where multiplication, shown $A.B$ or simply AB, has the special meaning of matrix multiplication, it must always be emphasized that although we use the familiar symbols of number algebra, nevertheless matrix algebra is a new algebra with new meanings given to the old symbols. In matrix multiplication the *position* of an element in row and column is of the utmost importance and for many purposes it is desirable to use a system to identify the row and column of an element. This can be done by adopting the convention that two suffix numbers are used so that the first suffix number identifies the row and the second suffix number identifies the column.

$$\begin{bmatrix} a_{11} & a_{12} \\ a_{21} & a_{22} \end{bmatrix}$$
a_{11} means the element in row 1 and column 1

a_{21} means the element in row 2 and column 1

The suffix number system has great advantages particularly in later work, but for a beginner the method used so far has other advantages.

When we come to regard matrices as a system of independent operators which can be regarded as having their own algebra without reference to the operations they represent, then the general definition of a matrix as an *array* of numbers is obviously acceptable. This definition was due to SYLVESTER a contemporary of CAYLEY and these two men are always remembered as the founders of modern matrix algebra and matrix notation.

In the next section we shall extend the ideas already developed to larger matrices that deal with mathematical quantities which require three ordered numbers to specify them, i.e. vectors of three dimensions.

C

Section III

Meaning of a (3×3) Matrix

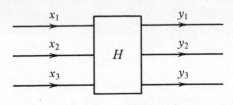

Diagram 21

Consider the network represented by H with three electrical inputs x_1, x_2, x_3 (these inputs could be e.m.f.s. or currents or a combination of both). The total input to H is a mathematical quantity specified by the three numbers x_1, x_2, x_3, i.e. the input is a vector of three

dimensions shown $\begin{bmatrix} x_1 \\ x_2 \\ x_3 \end{bmatrix}$ as a column matrix. If the outputs

y_1, y_2, y_3, are each a function of the input $\begin{bmatrix} x_1 \\ x_2 \\ x_3 \end{bmatrix}$ such that the

relation is *linear* then

$$y_1 = a_1 x_1 + b_1 x_2 + c_1 x_3$$
$$y_2 = a_2 x_1 + b_2 x_2 + c_2 x_3$$
$$y_3 = a_3 x_1 + b_3 x_2 + c_3 x_3$$

i.e.

$$\begin{bmatrix} y_1 \\ y_2 \\ y_3 \end{bmatrix} = \begin{bmatrix} a_1 & b_1 & c_1 \\ a_2 & b_2 & c_2 \\ a_3 & b_3 & c_3 \end{bmatrix} \begin{bmatrix} x_1 \\ x_2 \\ x_3 \end{bmatrix}$$

If Y is the column matrix $\begin{bmatrix} y_1 \\ y_2 \\ y_3 \end{bmatrix}$ X is the column matrix $\begin{bmatrix} x_1 \\ x_2 \\ x_3 \end{bmatrix}$ and

A now represents the matrix above, which has three rows and three columns, then

$$Y = A.X$$

A is called a (3×3) matrix and the column matrix X multiplied in matrix manner by the (3×3) matrix A gives the column matrix Y. Again the matrix represents the operation of the electrical network H on the inputs x_1, x_2, x_3 converting them into the outputs y_1, y_2, y_3.

Addition of (3×3) Matrices

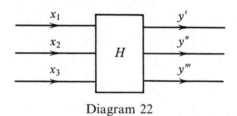

Diagram 22

Now suppose that the network H is adjusted to give a small output y', y'', y''', again depending on the inputs according to the linear relations

$$y' = a_1 x_1 + b_1 x_2 + c_1 x_3$$
$$y'' = a_2 x_1 + b_2 x_2 + c_2 x_3$$
$$y''' = a_3 x_1 + b_3 x_2 + c_3 x_3$$

In matrix form this is

$$\begin{bmatrix} y' \\ y'' \\ y''' \end{bmatrix} = \begin{bmatrix} a_1 & b_1 & c_1 \\ a_2 & b_2 & c_2 \\ a_3 & b_3 & c_3 \end{bmatrix} \begin{bmatrix} x_1 \\ x_2 \\ x_3 \end{bmatrix}$$

or $Y' = AX$.

Next suppose that an *additional* output is obtained calling these additional outputs y'_α, y''_β, y'''_γ, we then have

$$y'_\alpha = d_1 x_1 + e_1 x_2 + f_1 x_3$$
$$y''_\beta = d_2 x_1 + e_2 x_2 + f_2 x_3$$
$$y'''_\gamma = d_3 x_1 + e_3 x_2 + f_3 x_3$$

or

$$Y'' = \begin{bmatrix} d_1 & e_1 & f_1 \\ d_2 & e_2 & f_2 \\ d_3 & e_3 & f_3 \end{bmatrix} \begin{bmatrix} x_1 \\ x_2 \\ x_3 \end{bmatrix} = B.X$$

If the two outputs $\begin{bmatrix} y' \\ y'' \\ y''' \end{bmatrix}$ and $\begin{bmatrix} y'_\alpha \\ y''_\beta \\ y'''_\gamma \end{bmatrix}$ are now added to give the final

or total output $\begin{bmatrix} y_1 \\ y_2 \\ y_3 \end{bmatrix} = Y.$

$$y_1 = y' + y'_\alpha = (a_1 x_1 + b_1 x_2 + c_1 x_3) + (d_1 x_1 + e_1 x_2 + f_1 x_3)$$
$$y_2 = y'' + y''_\beta = (a_2 x_1 + b_2 x_2 + c_2 x_3) + (d_2 x_1 + e_2 x_2 + f_2 x_3)$$
$$y_3 = y''' + y'''_\gamma = (a_3 x_1 + b_3 x_2 + c_3 x_3) + (d_3 x_1 + e_3 x_2 + f_3 x_3)$$

$$\begin{bmatrix} y_1 \\ y_2 \\ y_3 \end{bmatrix} = \begin{matrix} (a_1 + d_1)x_1 + (b_1 + e_1)x_2 + (c_1 + f_1)x_3 \\ (a_2 + d_2)x_1 + (b_2 + e_2)x_2 + (c_2 + f_2)x_3 \\ (a_3 + d_3)x_1 + (b_3 + e_3)x_2 + (c_3 + f_3)x_3 \end{matrix}$$

$$Y = \begin{bmatrix} (a_1 + d_1) & (b_1 + e_1) & (c_1 + f_1) \\ (a_2 + d_2) & (b_2 + e_2) & (c_2 + f_2) \\ (a_3 + d_3) & (b_3 + e_3) & (c_3 + f_3) \end{bmatrix} X \qquad \dots (1)$$

But $Y = Y' + Y'' = AX + BX = (A + B)X$ from relation (1). Therefore as with (2×2) matrices so with (3×3) matrices, addition of two (3×3) matrices is carried out by the addition of corresponding elements and further the process shows again that

$$AX + B.X = (A + B)X$$

Scalar Multiplication

If $B = A$, i.e. the elements of B are equal to the corresponding elements of A then it follows that

$$A + A = \begin{bmatrix} 2a_1 & 2b_1 & 2c_1 \\ 2a_2 & 2b_2 & 2c_2 \\ 2a_3 & 2b_3 & 2c_3 \end{bmatrix}$$

$$\Rightarrow \quad 2A = \begin{bmatrix} 2a_1 & 2b_1 & 2c_1 \\ 2a_2 & 2b_2 & 2c_2 \\ 2a_3 & 2b_3 & 2c_3 \end{bmatrix}$$

Similarly $3A = 2A + A = \begin{bmatrix} 3a_1 & 3b_1 & 3c_1 \\ 3a_2 & 3b_2 & 3c_2 \\ 3a_3 & 3b_3 & 3c_3 \end{bmatrix}$.

The value of $k.A = \begin{bmatrix} ka_1 & kb_1 & kc_1 \\ ka_2 & kb_2 & kc_2 \\ ka_3 & kb_3 & kc_3 \end{bmatrix}$.

k is a pure number in the system and is called a SCALAR; kA is called scalar multiplication.

Subtraction of (3×3) Matrices

If in the network H the first output Y' had been followed by a *reduction* of output Y'' then the final output would have been Y.

$$Y = Y' - Y''$$

$$= AX - BX$$

$$= (A - B)X$$

and the process of subtraction would have given also

$$Y = \begin{bmatrix} (a_1 - d_1) & (b_1 - c_1) & (c_1 - f_1) \\ (a_2 - d_2) & (b_2 - c_2) & (c_2 - f_2) \\ (a_3 - d_3) & (b_3 - c_3) & (c_3 - f_3) \end{bmatrix} X$$

61

Hence subtraction of two matrices is carried out by the subtraction of elements of the second matrix from the corresponding elements of the first matrix.

$$\Rightarrow \quad A - B = A + (-B)$$

$$= A + (-1B) \quad \text{where } -1 \text{ is a scalar.}$$

Subtraction has been shown as a process of addition of negative elements.

Examples XIII

1 Express in matrix form

$$y_1 = 2x_1 + 3x_2 + 4x_3$$

$$y_2 = x_1 - 2x_2 + 3x_3$$

$$y_3 = 3x_1 + 2x_2 - 2x_3$$

2 Express as linear equations the matrix equation $Y = AX$, where $A = \begin{bmatrix} 3 & 2 & 1 \\ -2 & 3 & 6 \\ 1 & -2 & 4 \end{bmatrix}$, $Y = \begin{bmatrix} y_1 \\ y_2 \\ y_3 \end{bmatrix}$, $X = \begin{bmatrix} x_1 \\ x_2 \\ x_3 \end{bmatrix}$.

3 If $P = \begin{bmatrix} 1 & 2 & 1 \\ 3 & 2 & 1 \\ 2 & 3 & 2 \end{bmatrix}$ and $Q = \begin{bmatrix} 3 & 2 & 1 \\ 4 & 2 & 2 \\ 1 & 3 & 1 \end{bmatrix}$, find $P+Q$, $Q+P$, $Q-P$.

4 If $B = \begin{bmatrix} 1 & 2 & 1 \\ 3 & 2 & 3 \\ 2 & 1 & 2 \end{bmatrix}$, find $3B$ and kB.

5 If $P = \begin{bmatrix} 1 & 2 & 1 \\ 1 & 0 & 1 \\ 3 & 1 & 2 \end{bmatrix}$, $Q = \begin{bmatrix} 1 & 1 & 1 \\ 2 & 1 & 2 \\ 3 & 2 & 3 \end{bmatrix}$, $R = \begin{bmatrix} 1 & 0 & 1 \\ 2 & 1 & 3 \\ 1 & 2 & 3 \end{bmatrix}$, find

$P+Q$, $(P+Q)+R$, $(Q+R)$, $P+(Q+R)$. What can you say about $(P+Q)+R$ and $P+(Q+R)$?

Multiplication of (3×3) Matrices

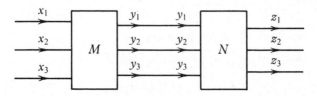

Diagram 23

Consider two separate circuits M and N so that the output of M becomes the input to N. If the operation of circuit M transforms the inputs x_1, x_2, x_3 into the outputs y_1, y_2, y_3 which in turn are transformed by circuit M into final outputs z_1, z_2, z_3, then using the notation of diagram 21

$$y_1 = a_1x_1 + b_1x_2 + c_1x_3 \qquad\qquad z_1 = d_1y_1 + e_1y_2 + f_1y_3$$
$$y_2 = a_2x_1 + b_2x_2 + c_2x_3 \quad \text{and} \quad z_2 = d_2y_1 + e_2y_2 + f_2y_2$$
$$y_3 = a_3x_1 + b_3x_2 + c_3x_3 \qquad\qquad z_3 = d_3y_1 + e_3y_2 + f_3y_3$$

In matrix notation

$$Y = A.X \quad \text{and} \quad Z = B.Y$$
$$\Rightarrow Z = B(AX) = B.A.X$$

but in algebraic notation

$$Z = z_1 = d_1(a_1x_1 + b_1x_2 + c_1x_3) + e_1(a_2x_1 + b_2x_2 + c_2x_3)$$
$$+ f_1(a_3x_1 + b_3x_2 + c_3x_3)$$

$$z_2 = d_2(a_1x_1 + b_1x_2 + c_1x_3) + e_2(a_2x_1 + b_2x_2 + c_2x_3)$$
$$+ f_2(a_3x_1 + b_3x_2 + c_3x_2)$$

$$z_3 = d_3(a_1x_1 + b_1x_2 + c_1x_3) + e_3(a_2x_1 + b_2x_2 + c_2x_3)$$
$$+ f_3(a_3x_2 + b_3x_2 + c_3x_3)$$

63

$$Z = \begin{bmatrix} z_1 \\ \\ \\ z_2 \\ \\ \\ \\ z_3 \end{bmatrix} \begin{aligned} &= (d_1a_1+e_1a_2+f_1a_3)x_1+(d_1b_1+e_1b_2+f_1b_3)x_2 \\ &\quad +(d_1c_1+e_1c_2+f_1c_3)x_3 \\ &= (d_2a_1+e_2a_2+f_2a_3)x_1+(d_2b_1+e_2b_2+f_2b_3)x_2 \\ &\quad +(d_2c_1+e_2c_2+f_2c_3)x_3 \\ &= (d_3a_1+e_3a_2+f_3a_3)x_1+(d_3b_1+e_3b_2+f_3b_3)x_2 \\ &\quad +(d_3c_1+e_3c_2+f_3c_3)x_3 \end{aligned}$$

adopting the scheme shown on page 14 this gives

$$= \begin{bmatrix} \boxed{d_1\ e_1\ f_1}\ \begin{matrix}a_1\\a_2\\a_3\end{matrix} & \boxed{d_1\ e_1\ f_1}\ \begin{matrix}b_1\\b_2\\b_3\end{matrix} & \boxed{d_1\ e_1\ f_1}\ \begin{matrix}c_1\\c_2\\c_3\end{matrix} \\ \boxed{d_2\ e_2\ f_2}\ \begin{matrix}a_1\\a_2\\a_3\end{matrix} & \boxed{d_2\ e_2\ f_2}\ \begin{matrix}b_1\\b_2\\b_3\end{matrix} & \boxed{d_2\ e_2\ f_2}\ \begin{matrix}c_1\\c_2\\c_3\end{matrix} \\ \boxed{d_3\ e_3\ f_3}\ \begin{matrix}a_1\\a_2\\a_3\end{matrix} & \boxed{d_3\ e_3\ f_3}\ \begin{matrix}b_1\\b_2\\b_3\end{matrix} & \boxed{d_3\ e_3\ f_3}\ \begin{matrix}c_1\\c_2\\c_3\end{matrix} \end{bmatrix} \begin{bmatrix} x_1 \\ \\ \\ x_2 \\ \\ \\ x_3 \end{bmatrix}$$

$$= \begin{bmatrix} (\text{Row}_1\text{ of }B)(\text{Col}_1\text{ of }A) & (R_1\text{ of }B)(C_2\text{ of }A) & (R_1\text{ of }B)(C_3\text{ of }A) \\ R_2C_1 & R_2C_2 & R_2C_3 \\ R_3C_1 & R_3C_2 & R_3C_3 \end{bmatrix} \begin{bmatrix} x_1 \\ x_2 \\ x_3 \end{bmatrix}$$

Hence multiplication of (3×3) matrices follows exactly the same form as matrix multiplication of (2×2) matrices, this being illustrated by a numerical example: —

$$P = \begin{bmatrix} 1 & 2 & 1 \\ 3 & 2 & 1 \\ 2 & 3 & 2 \end{bmatrix} \qquad Q = \begin{bmatrix} 3 & 2 & 1 \\ 1 & 1 & 2 \\ 1 & 2 & 1 \end{bmatrix}$$

If we multiply in the order $P.Q$ then we consider rows of P and columns of Q as with (2×2) matrices:

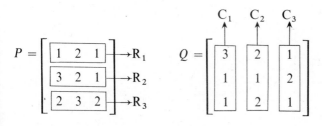

R_1, R_2, R_3 rows of P $\qquad$ C_1, C_2, C_3 columns of Q

then from the relation just established.

$$P.Q = \begin{bmatrix} R_1C_1 & R_1C_2 & R_1C_3 \\ R_2C_1 & R_2C_2 & R_2C_3 \\ R_3C_1 & R_3C_2 & R_3C_3 \end{bmatrix}$$

$$= \begin{bmatrix} \boxed{1 \ \ 2 \ \ 1} \ \begin{matrix} 3 \\ 1 \\ 1 \end{matrix} & \boxed{1 \ \ 2 \ \ 1} \ \begin{matrix} 2 \\ 1 \\ 2 \end{matrix} & \boxed{1 \ \ 2 \ \ 1} \ \begin{matrix} 1 \\ 2 \\ 1 \end{matrix} \\[3em] \boxed{3 \ \ 2 \ \ 1} \ \begin{matrix} 3 \\ 1 \\ 1 \end{matrix} & \boxed{3 \ \ 2 \ \ 1} \ \begin{matrix} 2 \\ 1 \\ 2 \end{matrix} & \boxed{3 \ \ 2 \ \ 1} \ \begin{matrix} 1 \\ 2 \\ 1 \end{matrix} \\[3em] \boxed{2 \ \ 3 \ \ 2} \ \begin{matrix} 3 \\ 1 \\ 1 \end{matrix} & \boxed{2 \ \ 3 \ \ 2} \ \begin{matrix} 2 \\ 1 \\ 2 \end{matrix} & \boxed{2 \ \ 3 \ \ 2} \ \begin{matrix} 1 \\ 2 \\ 1 \end{matrix} \end{bmatrix}$$

$$= \begin{bmatrix} \boxed{\begin{matrix} 1 \times 3 \\ 2 \times 1 \\ 1 \times 1 \end{matrix}} & \boxed{\begin{matrix} 1 \times 2 \\ 2 \times 1 \\ 1 \times 2 \end{matrix}} & \boxed{\begin{matrix} 1 \times 1 \\ 2 \times 2 \\ 1 \times 1 \end{matrix}} \\[4em] \boxed{\begin{matrix} 3 \times 3 \\ 2 \times 1 \\ 1 \times 1 \end{matrix}} & \boxed{\begin{matrix} 3 \times 2 \\ 2 \times 1 \\ 1 \times 2 \end{matrix}} & \boxed{\begin{matrix} 3 \times 1 \\ 2 \times 2 \\ 1 \times 1 \end{matrix}} \\[4em] \boxed{\begin{matrix} 2 \times 3 \\ 3 \times 1 \\ 2 \times 1 \end{matrix}} & \boxed{\begin{matrix} 2 \times 2 \\ 3 \times 1 \\ 2 \times 2 \end{matrix}} & \boxed{\begin{matrix} 2 \times 1 \\ 3 \times 2 \\ 2 \times 1 \end{matrix}} \end{bmatrix}$$

$$= \begin{bmatrix} 3+2+1 & 2+2+2 & 1+4+1 \\ 9+2+1 & 6+2+2 & 3+4+1 \\ 6+3+2 & 4+3+4 & 2+6+2 \end{bmatrix}$$

$$= \begin{bmatrix} 6 & 6 & 6 \\ 12 & 10 & 8 \\ 11 & 11 & 10 \end{bmatrix}$$

Notice that the multiplication of a (3×3) matrix by another (3×3) matrix results in a (3×3) matrix also. If we wish to repeat this process of matrix multiplication but post-multiplying Q by P, i.e. to find $Q \cdot P$, then the elements of Q must now be arranged in rows and the elements of P will in this case be arranged in columns as shown

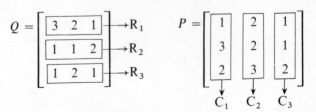

$$Q.P = \begin{bmatrix} R_1C_1 & R_1C_2 & R_1C_3 \\ R_2C_1 & R_2C_2 & R_2C_3 \\ R_3C_1 & R_3C_2 & R_3C_3 \end{bmatrix}$$

We can now proceed to the step showing the multiplication of elements.

$$= \begin{bmatrix} \boxed{\begin{matrix} 3\times1 \\ 2\times3 \\ 1\times2 \end{matrix}} & \boxed{\begin{matrix} 3\times2 \\ 2\times2 \\ 1\times3 \end{matrix}} & \boxed{\begin{matrix} 3\times1 \\ 2\times1 \\ 1\times2 \end{matrix}} \\ \boxed{\begin{matrix} 1\times1 \\ 1\times3 \\ 2\times2 \end{matrix}} & \boxed{\begin{matrix} 1\times2 \\ 1\times2 \\ 2\times3 \end{matrix}} & \boxed{\begin{matrix} 1\times1 \\ 1\times1 \\ 2\times2 \end{matrix}} \\ \boxed{\begin{matrix} 1\times1 \\ 2\times3 \\ 1\times2 \end{matrix}} & \boxed{\begin{matrix} 1\times2 \\ 2\times2 \\ 1\times3 \end{matrix}} & \boxed{\begin{matrix} 1\times1 \\ 2\times1 \\ 1\times2 \end{matrix}} \end{bmatrix}$$

$$= \begin{bmatrix} 3+6+2 & 6+4+3 & 3+2+2 \\ 1+3+4 & 2+2+6 & 1+1+4 \\ 1+6+2 & 2+4+3 & 1+2+2 \end{bmatrix}$$

$$= \begin{bmatrix} 11 & 13 & 7 \\ 8 & 10 & 6 \\ 9 & 9 & 5 \end{bmatrix}$$

It is obvious that the resulting (3×3) matrix from $Q.P$ is not the same as $P.Q$.

Once more the NON-COMMUTATIVE property of matrix algebra is illustrated for multiplication, but addition does follow the commutative law and we can show this with the two matrices P and Q.

$$P+Q = \begin{bmatrix} 1+3 & 2+2 & 1+1 \\ 3+1 & 2+1 & 1+2 \\ 2+1 & 3+2 & 2+1 \end{bmatrix}$$

67

$$\begin{bmatrix} 4 & 4 & 2 \\ 4 & 3 & 3 \\ 3 & 5 & 3 \end{bmatrix}$$

But since the elements are numbers the order of addition is not important, hence

$$Q+P = \begin{bmatrix} 4 & 4 & 2 \\ 4 & 3 & 3 \\ 3 & 5 & 3 \end{bmatrix}$$

and therefore $P+Q = Q+P$.

The Null or Zero Matrix

As with (2×2) matrices the NULL or ZERO matrix for (3×3) matrices is $\begin{bmatrix} 0 & 0 & 0 \\ 0 & 0 & 0 \\ 0 & 0 & 0 \end{bmatrix} = 0.$

Addition of elements gives $P+0 = P$

$$\text{and } 0+P = P$$

Multiplication of P by 0 must result in zero elements and hence the product is a zero or null matrix

$$P.0 = 0.P = 0$$

The Unit (3×3) Matrix

With (2×2) matrices, the array $\begin{bmatrix} 1 & 0 \\ 0 & 1 \end{bmatrix}$ behaves as the UNIT

MATRIX, it is reasonable to suppose that the matrix $\begin{bmatrix} 1 & 0 & 0 \\ 0 & 1 & 0 \\ 0 & 0 & 1 \end{bmatrix}$

behaves in the same way with (3×3) matrices.

This can be tested with a numerical matrix.

Let $A = \begin{bmatrix} 1 & 2 & 3 \\ 2 & 1 & 1 \\ 1 & 3 & 2 \end{bmatrix}$

$$\begin{bmatrix} 1 & 2 & 3 \\ 2 & 1 & 1 \\ 1 & 3 & 2 \end{bmatrix} \begin{bmatrix} 1 & 0 & 0 \\ 0 & 1 & 0 \\ 0 & 0 & 1 \end{bmatrix} = \begin{bmatrix} 1 & 2 & 3 \\ 2 & 1 & 1 \\ 1 & 3 & 2 \end{bmatrix} = A$$

Post-multiplication by $\begin{bmatrix} 1 & 0 & 0 \\ 0 & 1 & 0 \\ 0 & 0 & 1 \end{bmatrix}$ has left A unchanged. Again,

pre-multiplication gives

$$\begin{bmatrix} 1 & 0 & 0 \\ 0 & 1 & 0 \\ 0 & 0 & 1 \end{bmatrix} \begin{bmatrix} 1 & 2 & 3 \\ 2 & 1 & 1 \\ 1 & 3 & 2 \end{bmatrix} = \begin{bmatrix} 1 & 2 & 3 \\ 2 & 1 & 1 \\ 1 & 3 & 2 \end{bmatrix} = A$$

The matrix $\begin{bmatrix} 1 & 0 & 0 \\ 0 & 1 & 0 \\ 0 & 0 & 1 \end{bmatrix}$ has behaved like the unit number of

number algebra, the matrix is called the UNIT MATRIX for (3×3) matrices and again is denoted by I.

$$A.I = IA = A$$

Taking the general matrix $M = \begin{bmatrix} a_1 & b_1 & c_1 \\ a_2 & b_2 & c_2 \\ a_3 & b_3 & c_3 \end{bmatrix}$ post- or pre-

multiplication by I always yields an unchanged matrix.

$$\begin{bmatrix} a_1 & b_1 & c_1 \\ a_2 & b_2 & c_2 \\ a_3 & b_3 & c_3 \end{bmatrix} \begin{bmatrix} 1 & 0 & 0 \\ 0 & 1 & 0 \\ 0 & 0 & 1 \end{bmatrix} = \begin{bmatrix} a_1 & b_1 & c_1 \\ a_2 & b_2 & c_2 \\ a_3 & b_3 & c_3 \end{bmatrix} = M$$

$$\begin{bmatrix} 1 & 0 & 0 \\ 0 & 1 & 0 \\ 0 & 0 & 1 \end{bmatrix} \begin{bmatrix} a_1 & b_1 & c_1 \\ a_2 & b_2 & c_2 \\ a_3 & b_3 & c_3 \end{bmatrix} = \begin{bmatrix} a_1 & b_1 & c_1 \\ a_2 & b_2 & c_2 \\ a_3 & b_3 & c_3 \end{bmatrix} = M$$

$M . I = I . M = M$ for all the different Ms.

The Scalar Matrix

The matrix $\begin{bmatrix} k & 0 & 0 \\ 0 & k & 0 \\ 0 & 0 & k \end{bmatrix}$ is called the SCALAR matrix and is

obviously obtained by the scalar multiplication of matrix I by k

$$kI = \begin{bmatrix} k & 0 & 0 \\ 0 & k & 0 \\ 0 & 0 & k \end{bmatrix}$$

The Diagonal Matrix

The SCALAR matrix is a special case of a DIAGONAL matrix. In a diagonal matrix all the elements except those on the leading diagonal are zeros.

$\begin{bmatrix} 2 & 0 & 0 \\ 0 & 3 & 0 \\ 0 & 0 & 1 \end{bmatrix}$ is a simple example of a diagonal matrix.

Examples XIV

1 $P = \begin{bmatrix} 1 & 2 & 1 \\ 3 & 2 & 1 \\ 2 & 3 & 2 \end{bmatrix}$ $Q = \begin{bmatrix} 3 & 2 & 1 \\ 4 & 2 & 2 \\ 1 & 3 & 1 \end{bmatrix}$

Find $Q.P$ and $P.Q$. What does this illustrate?

2 $B = \begin{bmatrix} 1 & 1 & 2 \\ 2 & 3 & 2 \\ 1 & 2 & 1 \end{bmatrix}$ $I = \begin{bmatrix} 1 & 0 & 0 \\ 0 & 1 & 0 \\ 0 & 0 & 1 \end{bmatrix}$

Find $BI, kI, B+kI, B-kI$.

3 $P = \begin{bmatrix} 1 & 2 & 1 \\ 1 & 0 & 1 \\ 3 & 1 & 2 \end{bmatrix}$ $Q = \begin{bmatrix} 1 & 0 & 1 \\ 2 & 1 & -2 \\ 3 & 2 & 3 \end{bmatrix}$ $R = \begin{bmatrix} 1 & 0 & -1 \\ 2 & 1 & 3 \\ 1 & 2 & 3 \end{bmatrix}$

Find PQ, $(PQ)R$, QR, $P(QR)$, $P(RQ)$, $R(PQ)$. What conclusions can be drawn from these calculations?

4 $A = \begin{bmatrix} 3 & 2 & 1 \\ -2 & 3 & 6 \\ 1 & -2 & 4 \end{bmatrix}$ $S = \begin{bmatrix} 2 & 0 & 0 \\ 0 & 3 & 0 \\ 0 & 0 & 4 \end{bmatrix}$ $T = \begin{bmatrix} 2 & 0 & 0 \\ 0 & -3 & 0 \\ 0 & 0 & -4 \end{bmatrix}$

Find AS, AT, SA, TA, S^2, ST.

5 $A = \begin{bmatrix} 3 & 2 & 1 \\ -2 & 3 & 6 \\ 1 & -2 & 4 \end{bmatrix}$ $V = \begin{bmatrix} 0 & 0 & 1 \\ 0 & 1 & 0 \\ 1 & 0 & 0 \end{bmatrix}$

Find AV and VA.

Geometrical Transformation of a (3×3) Matrix

Just as (2×2) matrices cause transformations in geometrical figures of two dimensions, i.e. areas, so (3×3) matrices operating in three dimensions transform figures which are solids into new shapes.

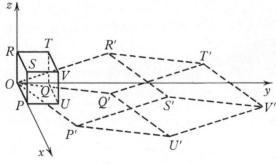

Diagram 24

71

We shall consider the unit cube using three mutually perpendicular axes ox, oy, oz, using a right-handed system as shown in the diagram.

The points O, P, Q, R, S, T, U, V, defining the unit cube have the co-ordinates given in the table together with the co-ordinates of their images caused by the matrix transformation

$$\begin{bmatrix} x' \\ y' \\ z' \end{bmatrix} = \begin{bmatrix} 2 & 1 & 1 \\ 1 & 2 & 2 \\ 1 & 3 & 2 \end{bmatrix} \begin{bmatrix} x \\ y \\ z \end{bmatrix}$$

or

$$x' = 2x + y + z$$
$$y' = x + 2y + 2z$$
$$z' = x + 3y + 2z$$

O	P	Q	R	S	T	U	V
0, 0, 0	1, 0, 0	0, 1, 0	0, 0, 1	1, 0, 1	0, 1, 1	1, 1, 0	1, 1, 1
O'	P'	Q'	R'	S'	T'	U'	V'
0, 0, 0	2, 1, 1	1, 2, 3	1, 2, 2	3, 3, 3	2, 4, 5	3, 3, 4	4, 5, 6

These points when plotted in space give a figure whose faces are no longer squares but parallelograms and so the new solid is called a PARALLELEPIPED. The (3×3) matrix has transformed a unit cube into a parallelepiped of three dimensions. When considering the geometrical transformation caused by a (2×2) matrix we found that the area of the transformed figure and the area of the unit square were in the ratio equal to the value of the determinant of the matrix. When dealing with the (3×3) matrix the volume of the parallelepiped and the volume of the unit cube can be shown to be in the ratio equal to the determinant of the (3×3) matrix.

If the transformed parallelepiped $OP'Q'V'R'S'U'T'$ is transformed by the second application of the matrix it is found that the new parallelepiped would have its volume increased again in the ratio of the value of the determinant since the solid $OP'Q'V'R'S'U'T'$ could be considered as being composed of a number of unit volumes each of which would be increased in the ratio of the determinant and the new volume would be the sum of the parallelepipeds from each of these unit cubes.

The Calculation of the Determinant of a (3×3) Matrix

Historically the idea of a determinant arose in the solution of linear equations and was found to be the value of the products resulting from the number of arrangements of the coefficients so that each coefficient came from a *different row and column* and was also given its appropriate positive or negative sign according to its position: we shall now proceed to demonstrate this.

So with a (3×3) matrix the determinant formed from its elements must come from the *arrangement* of the elements taken *three* at a time since there are three rows and three columns.

For the (3×3) matrix $\begin{bmatrix} a_1 & b_1 & c_1 \\ a_2 & b_2 & c_2 \\ a_3 & b_3 & c_3 \end{bmatrix}$ Row 1 if we select the

Column 1

element a_1 which is in column 1 and row 1 the elements not in its row or column are $\begin{vmatrix} b_2 & c_2 \\ b_3 & c_3 \end{vmatrix}$ forming a (2×2) determinant.

This (2×2) determinant is called the MINOR of element a_1. To find the *minor* of element b_1 we strike out the elements in its row 1 and column 2 leaving the elements $\begin{vmatrix} a_2 & c_2 \\ a_3 & c_3 \end{vmatrix}$ to form its minor.

Every element of the matrix has its own *minor* and the determinant value of these minors can be calculated as shown earlier. Next if we give to each minor a positive or negative sign according to the *position* of the *element* of which it is the minor, shown by the pattern

$$\begin{bmatrix} + & - & + \\ - & + & - \\ + & - & + \end{bmatrix}$$

then these *signed-minors* are called CO-FACTORS.

In our matrix $\begin{bmatrix} a_1 & b_1 & c_1 \\ a_2 & b_2 & c_2 \\ a_3 & b_3 & c_3 \end{bmatrix}$ the CO-FACTOR of a_1 is $+\begin{vmatrix} b_2 & c_2 \\ b_3 & c_3 \end{vmatrix}$

$= +(b_2 c_3 - b_3 c_2)$ shown A_1,

the CO-FACTOR of element b_1 is $-\begin{vmatrix} a_2 & c_2 \\ a_3 & c_3 \end{vmatrix} = -(a_2c_3 - a_3c_2)$

shown B_1,

the CO-FACTOR of element c_1 is $+\begin{vmatrix} a_2 & b_2 \\ a_3 & b_3 \end{vmatrix} = +(a_2b_3 - a_3b_2)$

shown C_1.

Definition of Determinant

The value of the DETERMINANT is $a_1A + b_1B + c_1C$ which when multiplied out gives six products each formed from three elements:

$$a_1(b_2c_3 - b_3c_2) + b_1\{-(a_2c_3 - a_3c_2)\} + c_1(a_2b_3 - a_3b_2)$$
$$= a_1b_2c_3 + a_3b_1c_2 + a_2b_3c_1 - a_1b_3c_2 - a_2b_1c_3 - a_3b_2c_1$$

Any row or column could have been used for the calculation of the determinant; had the first column been used, the value would have been

$$a_1A_1 + a_2A_2 + a_3A_3 = a_1\begin{vmatrix} b_2 & c_2 \\ b_3 & c_3 \end{vmatrix} + a_2\left\{-\begin{vmatrix} b_1 & c_1 \\ b_3 & c_3 \end{vmatrix}\right\} + a_3\begin{vmatrix} b_1 & c_1 \\ b_2 & c_2 \end{vmatrix}.$$
$$= a_1(b_2c_3 - b_3c_2 - a_2(b_1c_3 - b_3c_1) + a_3(b_1c_2 - b_2c_1)$$
$$= a_1b_2c_3 + a_2b_3c_1 + a_3b_1c_2 - a_1b_3c_2 - a_2b_1c_3 - a_3b_2c_1$$

and this result is exactly equal to the previous value when the elements of the first row were chosen. The determinant when found is a pure number (a scalar).

Example

Find the determinant of the matrix $\begin{bmatrix} 1 & 2 & 1 \\ 2 & 4 & 6 \\ 3 & 1 & 2 \end{bmatrix}$. The determinant

is shown $\begin{vmatrix} 1 & 2 & 1 \\ 2 & 4 & 6 \\ 3 & 1 & 2 \end{vmatrix}$ using the same notation as with (2×2) matrices.

(This notation was first introduced by Cayley in 1853.)

Taking the elements of the first row   1   2   1   their co-factors are $+\begin{vmatrix} 4 & 6 \\ 1 & 2 \end{vmatrix}$, $-\begin{vmatrix} 2 & 6 \\ 3 & 2 \end{vmatrix}$ and $+\begin{vmatrix} 2 & 4 \\ 3 & 1 \end{vmatrix}$ or $(8-6)$, $-(4-18)$ and $(2-12)$ i.e. $+2$, $+14$ and -10.

$$\text{Determinant } (\triangle) = (1 \times +2) + 2(+14) + (1 \times -10)$$
$$= 2 + 28 - 10 = +20$$

The matrix used in the geometrical transformation on page 72 shown in diagram 24 is $\begin{bmatrix} 2 & 1 & 1 \\ 1 & 2 & 2 \\ 1 & 3 & 2 \end{bmatrix}$.

$\begin{vmatrix} 2 & 1 & 1 \\ 1 & 2 & 2 \\ 1 & 3 & 2 \end{vmatrix}$ is the determinant of this matrix, call it $\triangle$.

$\triangle = 2\begin{vmatrix} 2 & 2 \\ 3 & 2 \end{vmatrix} - 1\begin{vmatrix} 1 & 2 \\ 1 & 2 \end{vmatrix} + 1\begin{vmatrix} 1 & 2 \\ 1 & 3 \end{vmatrix}$ note the negative sign of the second term.

$$= 2(4-6) - 1(2-2) + 1(3-2)$$

$$= -4 + 0 + 1$$

$$= -3$$

The volume of the parallelepiped is three times that of the unit cube (the negative sign has no significance with respect to volume but affects the position of the solid in space).

When the determinant of a (3×3) matrix is zero the matrix is said to be SINGULAR and the transformation it represents causes the IMAGES of the eight points defining the unit cube to fall on a plane, i.e. the volume of the transformation is zero also and the images then define an area if only two rows or two columns are in the same ratio, as with the matrix $\begin{bmatrix} 2 & 1 & 1 \\ 1 & 2 & 2 \\ 2 & 4 & 4 \end{bmatrix}$. The determinant is zero and rows 2 and 3 result in the y', z' of the transformed points being in a constant ratio of $1:2$. All the points of this transform will lie in a plane which passes through the point O, O, O (the origin) and cuts the yz plane in a straight line which passes through the origin and has the equation $z = 2y$, this is shown in diagram 25.

Since all the images of the points O, P, V, Q, R, S, U, T, lie in the plane shown, the figure has degenerated from a parallelepiped having volume, to a plane area. The singular matrix has resulted in an image of three-dimensional space in two-dimensional space. This topic will be dealt with in another aspect later, when the subject of Linear Dependence is studied.

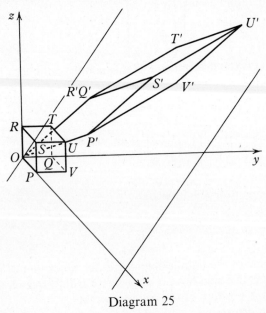

Diagram 25

Although we have shown that the operation represented by a (3×3) matrix has a geometrical meaning we can consider (3×3) matrices as an independent system having an algebra of their own as was done earlier with (2×2) matrices. We now proceed to a study of these matrices independent of the operations which they represent.

Examples XV

1 Find the value of the determinant $|P| = \begin{vmatrix} 1 & 2 & 1 \\ 3 & 2 & 1 \\ 2 & 3 & 1 \end{vmatrix}$ of the matrix $P = \begin{bmatrix} 1 & 2 & 1 \\ 3 & 2 & 1 \\ 2 & 3 & 2 \end{bmatrix}$.

2 Find the value of the determinant $|Q|$ of the matrix
$Q = \begin{bmatrix} 3 & 2 & 1 \\ 4 & 2 & 2 \\ 1 & 3 & 1 \end{bmatrix}$.

3 Find the value of the determinant $|A|$ of the matrix
$A = \begin{bmatrix} 1 & 0 & 3 \\ 2 & 1 & 4 \\ 0 & 1 & 3 \end{bmatrix}$.

4 Is the matrix $B = \begin{bmatrix} 2 & 1 & 1 \\ 1 & 2 & 2 \\ 2 & 4 & 4 \end{bmatrix}$ singular or non-singular? (Hint:

find the value of its determinant $|B|$.)

5 Using the matrices A and B of questions 3 and 4, find $C = A.B$, then find the determinant of matrix C. Is matrix C singular or non-singular?

6 Find the determinant of $\begin{bmatrix} 2 & 0 & 0 \\ 0 & 2 & 0 \\ 0 & 0 & 2 \end{bmatrix}$.

7 Find the determinant of $\begin{bmatrix} 2 & 0 & 0 \\ 0 & 3 & 0 \\ 0 & 0 & 4 \end{bmatrix}$.

8 Find the determinant of $D = \begin{bmatrix} 1 & 0 & 0 \\ 2 & 2 & 0 \\ 4 & 3 & 2 \end{bmatrix}$ and $E = \begin{bmatrix} 1 & 0 & 0 \\ 0 & 2 & 0 \\ 0 & 0 & 2 \end{bmatrix}$.

The Transpose of a Matrix

The TRANSPOSE of a matrix A is that matrix whose rows are the columns of A and whose columns are the rows of A and is denoted by A' or A^t

$$A = \begin{bmatrix} a_1 & b_1 & c_1 \\ a_2 & b_2 & c_2 \\ a_3 & b_3 & c_3 \end{bmatrix} \qquad A^t = \begin{bmatrix} a_1 & a_2 & a_3 \\ b_1 & b_2 & b_3 \\ c_1 & c_2 & c_3 \end{bmatrix}$$

Inspection shows that the elements along the LEADING DIAGONAL are unchanged in position and since we can calculate the value of the determinant using the elements of a row or the elements of a column then the determinant value must remain unaltered.

If we denote the determinant of the matrix A by the symbol $|A|$ then

$$|A| = |A^t|$$

If the transpose of a matrix gives a matrix which is equal to the original, such a matrix is said to be SYMMETRIC.

Example

$$Q = \begin{bmatrix} 1 & 2 & 3 \\ 2 & 4 & 1 \\ 3 & 1 & 2 \end{bmatrix} \qquad Q^t = \begin{bmatrix} 1 & 2 & 3 \\ 2 & 4 & 1 \\ 3 & 1 & 2 \end{bmatrix}$$

$$Q = Q^t$$

Q is symmetric.

The Adjoint Matrix

Definition

The matrix formed by transposing the elements formed from the CO-FACTORS is called the ADJOINT matrix.

For the matrix $A = \begin{bmatrix} 1 & 2 & 1 \\ 2 & 4 & 6 \\ 3 & 1 & 2 \end{bmatrix}$ used in the example in page 74 the co-factors of the elements are by calculation of the minors

$$\begin{bmatrix} 2 & 14 & -10 \\ -3 & -1 & 5 \\ 8 & -4 & 0 \end{bmatrix}.$$

The Adjoint matrix is formed by transposing the rows and columns.

Adjoint matrix is $\begin{bmatrix} 2 & -3 & 8 \\ 14 & -1 & -4 \\ -10 & 5 & 0 \end{bmatrix}.$

Now this Adjoint matrix has very special properties in relation to the matrix A from which it was formed and the Unit matrix I. This will be shown by multiplication.

$$A.[\text{Adjoint } A] = \begin{bmatrix} 1 & 2 & 1 \\ 2 & 4 & 6 \\ 3 & 1 & 2 \end{bmatrix}\begin{bmatrix} 2 & -3 & 8 \\ 14 & -1 & -4 \\ -10 & 5 & 0 \end{bmatrix}$$

$$\begin{bmatrix} 20 & 0 & 0 \\ 0 & 20 & 0 \\ 0 & 0 & 20 \end{bmatrix}$$

$$= 20\begin{bmatrix} 1 & 0 & 0 \\ 0 & 1 & 0 \\ 0 & 0 & 1 \end{bmatrix}$$

$$= 20I$$

$$\Rightarrow A.\left[\frac{\text{Adjoint } A}{20}\right] = I \qquad \qquad \dots \text{(i)}$$

But on page 75 we showed the determinant of A to be 20

$$\Rightarrow A\left[\frac{\text{Adjoint } A}{|A|}\right] = I$$

Next we find

$$\left[\frac{\text{Adj}.A}{|A|}\right]\left[A\right] = \frac{1}{20}\begin{bmatrix} 2 & -3 & 8 \\ 14 & -1 & -4 \\ -10 & 5 & 0 \end{bmatrix}\begin{bmatrix} 1 & 2 & 1 \\ 2 & 4 & 6 \\ 3 & 1 & 2 \end{bmatrix}$$

79

$$= \frac{1}{20}\begin{bmatrix} 20 & 0 & 0 \\ 0 & 20 & 0 \\ 0 & 0 & 20 \end{bmatrix}$$

$$= \begin{bmatrix} 1 & 0 & 0 \\ 0 & 1 & 0 \\ 0 & 0 & 1 \end{bmatrix}$$

$$= I \qquad\qquad \ldots \text{(ii)}$$

$$\left[A\right]\left[\frac{\text{Adjoint } A}{|A|}\right] = I \text{ (shown at (i))}$$

and $\left[\dfrac{\text{Adjoint } A}{|A|}\right]\left[A\right] = I$ (shown at (ii))

The matrix $\left[\dfrac{\text{Adjoint } A}{|A|}\right]$ can also be written $\dfrac{1}{|A|}\left[\text{Adjoint } A\right]$

since the determinant $|A|$ is a number, i.e. a scalar, and this matrix has special properties since pre-multiplication or post-multiplication of A by this matrix results in the unit matrix. It is unique and is the INVERSE of A, i.e. A^{-1}.

$$A^{-1} = \left[\frac{\text{Adjoint } A}{|A|}\right]$$

If for any (3×3) matrix the determinant is zero then the INVERSE of that matrix cannot be defined. Such a matrix has already been termed a SINGULAR matrix. But for all *non-singular* matrices the inverse matrix can always be calculated from the Adjoint matrix as shown. [The method holds for all *non-singular* square matrices of higher orders also—it is a general method for square matrices of any order but at this stage we are only concerned with (3×3) matrices.]

Examples XVI

1 Find the TRANSPOSE A^t of $A = \begin{bmatrix} 1 & 2 & 3 \\ 3 & 2 & 1 \\ 2 & 3 & 2 \end{bmatrix}$.

2 Find the transpose B^t (or B') of $B = \begin{bmatrix} 3 & 2 & 1 \\ -2 & 3 & 6 \\ 1 & -2 & 4 \end{bmatrix}$.

3 In questions 1 and 2 compare the leading diagonal of A^t with that of A and of B^t with that of B. What conclusion do you draw?

4 Form the matrix C whose elements are the CO-FACTORS of the elements of $Q = \begin{bmatrix} 3 & 2 & 1 \\ 4 & 2 & 2 \\ 1 & 3 & 1 \end{bmatrix}$, then by transposing the elements

of C find [ADJOINT Q]. Calculate the determinant of Q, i.e. $|Q|$. Hence state Q^{-1} and verify that $QQ^{-1} = Q^{-1}Q = I$.

5 Find A^{-1} and verify $A^{-1}.A = A.A^{-1} = I$ when

$$A = \begin{bmatrix} 1 & 0 & 3 \\ 2 & 1 & 4 \\ 0 & 1 & 3 \end{bmatrix}.$$

6 If $P = \begin{bmatrix} 1 & 2 & 1 \\ 3 & 2 & 1 \\ 2 & 3 & 2 \end{bmatrix}$ find P^{-1} and verify.

7 If $R = \begin{bmatrix} -1 & 2 & 0 \\ -3 & 1 & 2 \\ 3 & 0 & -4 \end{bmatrix}$ find R^{-1} and verify.

8 If $A = \begin{bmatrix} a & h & g \\ h & b & f \\ g & f & c \end{bmatrix}$ write out the transpose of A. What do you

notice about A^t and A?

9 If $P = \begin{bmatrix} 1 & 2 & 1 \\ 1 & 0 & 1 \\ 3 & 1 & 2 \end{bmatrix}$ $Q = \begin{bmatrix} 1 & 1 & 1 \\ 2 & 1 & 2 \\ 3 & 2 & 3 \end{bmatrix}$ find PQ, P', Q', QP,

$P'Q'$, $Q'P'$, $(PQ)'$, $(QP)'$ and show that

$$(PQ)' = Q'P'$$

$$(QP)' = P'Q'.$$

$$(P' = P^t \quad \text{Alternative symbols}).$$

10 If $P = \begin{bmatrix} 1 & 2 & 1 \\ 1 & 0 & 1 \\ 3 & 1 & 2 \end{bmatrix}$, $Q = \begin{bmatrix} 1 & 1 & 1 \\ 2 & 1 & 2 \\ 3 & 2 & 3 \end{bmatrix}$, $R = \begin{bmatrix} 1 & 0 & 1 \\ 2 & 1 & 3 \\ 1 & 2 & 3 \end{bmatrix}$, find

PQR, QR, P', $(QR)'P$, $R'Q'$, $R'Q'P'$ and hence show that

$$(PQR)' = (QR)'P'$$

$$= R'Q'P' \dots \text{(the Reversal Rule)}$$

$$(P' = P^t \quad P' \text{ means } P^t)$$

The Solution of Three Simultaneous Equations Using Matrix Method

If

$$\left. \begin{array}{r} -x+2y-3z = -8 \\ 2x-y+4z = 17 \\ 3x+4y+z = 22 \end{array} \right\}$$

then

$$\begin{bmatrix} -1 & 2 & -3 \\ 2 & -1 & 4 \\ 2 & 4 & 1 \end{bmatrix} \begin{bmatrix} x \\ y \\ z \end{bmatrix} = \begin{bmatrix} -8 \\ 17 \\ 22 \end{bmatrix} \qquad \dots \text{(i)}$$

$$A \begin{bmatrix} x \\ y \\ z \end{bmatrix} = \begin{bmatrix} -8 \\ 17 \\ 22 \end{bmatrix} \quad \text{If the } 3 \times 3 \text{ matrix is represented by } A.$$

We now calculate the inverse of A in three steps.

(i) Determinant of

$$A = |A| = -1(-1-16) - 2(2-12) - 3(8+3) = 4.$$

(ii) Adj. $A = \begin{bmatrix} -17 & 10 & 11 \\ -14 & 8 & 10 \\ 5 & -2 & -3 \end{bmatrix}^t = \begin{bmatrix} -17 & -14 & 5 \\ 10 & 8 & -2 \\ 11 & 10 & -3 \end{bmatrix}$

(iii) $A^{-1} = \left[\dfrac{\text{Adj.}\,A}{|A|}\right] = \dfrac{1}{4}\begin{bmatrix} -17 & -14 & 5 \\ -10 & 8 & -2 \\ 11 & 10 & -3 \end{bmatrix}$

We now pre-multiply both sides of the matrix equation (i)

$$\frac{1}{4}\begin{bmatrix} -17 & -14 & 5 \\ 10 & 8 & -2 \\ 11 & 10 & -3 \end{bmatrix}\begin{bmatrix} -1 & 2 & -3 \\ 2 & -1 & 4 \\ 3 & 4 & 1 \end{bmatrix}\begin{bmatrix} x \\ y \\ z \end{bmatrix} = \frac{1}{4}\begin{bmatrix} -17 & -14 & 5 \\ 10 & 8 & -2 \\ 11 & 10 & -3 \end{bmatrix}\begin{bmatrix} -8 \\ 17 \\ 22 \end{bmatrix}$$

$$\Rightarrow \frac{1}{4}\begin{bmatrix} 4 & 0 & 0 \\ 0 & 4 & 0 \\ 0 & 0 & 4 \end{bmatrix}\begin{bmatrix} x \\ y \\ z \end{bmatrix} = \frac{1}{4}\begin{bmatrix} 8 \\ 12 \\ 16 \end{bmatrix}$$

$$\Rightarrow \begin{bmatrix} 1 & 0 & 0 \\ 0 & 1 & 0 \\ 0 & 0 & 1 \end{bmatrix}\begin{bmatrix} x \\ y \\ z \end{bmatrix} = \begin{bmatrix} 2 \\ 3 \\ 4 \end{bmatrix}$$

$$\Rightarrow \begin{bmatrix} x \\ y \\ z \end{bmatrix} = \begin{bmatrix} 2 \\ 3 \\ 4 \end{bmatrix}$$

For these two column matrices to be equal, their corresponding elements must be equal

$$\Rightarrow \left.\begin{array}{r} x = 2 \\ y = 3 \\ z = 4 \end{array}\right\}$$

The result can be checked by substitution or by working in the normal algebraic method. We would not normally use the matrix method for this kind of problem, but at a later stage where machine or computer facilities are available similar applications are possible.

83

Manufacturers of desk calculating machines often supply instructions with the machines for this type of matrix solution and hold short courses at many centres on the subject. With large electronic computers other methods are available when equations with hundreds of unknowns have to be solved, but these methods are only understood after matrix methods have been mastered.

Examples XVII

1 Express the equations in matrix form $P\begin{bmatrix} x \\ y \\ z \end{bmatrix} = \begin{bmatrix} 0 \\ 2 \\ 2 \end{bmatrix}$

$$x + 2y + z = 0$$
$$3x + 2y + z = 2$$
$$2x + 3y + 2z = 2$$

then find P^{-1} and solve the equations using the matrix method.

2 Express the equations

$$-x + 2y = 5$$
$$-3x + y + 2z = -1$$
$$3x \quad -4z = +9$$

in matrix form and find the solutions using matrix methods.

3 If $Q = \begin{bmatrix} 3 & 2 & 1 \\ 4 & 2 & 2 \\ 1 & 3 & 1 \end{bmatrix}$ and $Q\begin{bmatrix} x \\ y \\ z \end{bmatrix} = \begin{bmatrix} 16 \\ 22 \\ 15 \end{bmatrix}$, find the set of solutions by matrix methods.

4 Solve

$$\left. \begin{array}{r} x + 3z = 7 \\ 2x + y + 4z = 13 \\ 2y + 3z = 12 \end{array} \right\}$$

by matrix methods.

Product of Two Matrices and their Determinants

On page 74 matrix $A = \begin{bmatrix} 1 & 2 & 1 \\ 2 & 4 & 6 \\ 3 & 1 & 2 \end{bmatrix}$ has a determinant value of

20 (found on page 75), we call the matrix $B = \begin{bmatrix} -1 & 2 & -3 \\ 2 & -1 & 4 \\ 3 & 4 & 1 \end{bmatrix}$

which was used on page 82 and has determinant 4, i.e. $|A| = 20$ and $|B| = 4$.

Next we find $A.B$ and $B.A$:

$$A.B = \begin{bmatrix} 1 & 2 & 1 \\ 2 & 4 & 6 \\ 3 & 1 & 2 \end{bmatrix} \begin{bmatrix} -1 & 2 & -3 \\ 2 & -1 & 4 \\ 3 & 4 & 1 \end{bmatrix} = \begin{bmatrix} 6 & 4 & 6 \\ 24 & 24 & 16 \\ 5 & 13 & -3 \end{bmatrix}$$

If we call this matrix C such that $A.B = C$ we now find that $|C| = 80$ but $|A| = 20$ and $|B| = 4$.

$\Rightarrow |A|.|B| = |C|$ although matrix C is a new matrix obtained by pre-multiplying B by A.

Next we find the product $B.A = D$

$$B.A = \begin{bmatrix} -1 & 2 & -3 \\ 2 & -1 & 4 \\ 3 & 4 & 1 \end{bmatrix} \begin{bmatrix} 1 & 2 & 1 \\ 2 & 4 & 6 \\ 3 & 1 & 2 \end{bmatrix} = \begin{bmatrix} -6 & 3 & 5 \\ 12 & 4 & 4 \\ 14 & 23 & 29 \end{bmatrix}$$

The matrix D is obtained by post-multiplying B by A and is obviously different from C.

Once more we have shown that $A.B \neq B.A$.

But although multiplication of matrices is non-commutative since the value of $|D| = 80$, $|B|.|A| = |D|$. Generally,

$$|A|.|B| = |A.B|$$

and

$$|B|.|A| = |B.A| = |A.B|.$$

Thus the multiplication of the determinants does follow the commutative law and this must be so, because $|A|$, $|B|$, $|D|$, $|C|$ are all scalar numbers and so follow the laws of number algebra.

In the algebra of (2×2) matrices it was shown that the product of any matrix with a SINGULAR matrix gave a singular matrix as the product. We have now demonstrated that the product of two (3×3) matrices has a determinant which is the product of the determinants of the two separate matrices. This is always true and hence with all matrices the product of a matrix with a singular matrix is always a singular matrix. This result is important and has many implications in later work and we shall use this property when dealing with the characteristic equation of a matrix, which has many applications especially in quantum mechanics.

The Calculation of Determinants of the Third Order

It was shown earlier that for the third order determinant $\begin{vmatrix} a_1 & b_1 & c_1 \\ a_2 & b_2 & c_2 \\ a_3 & b_3 & c_3 \end{vmatrix}$ the value of the determinant $\triangle$ is $a_1A_1 + b_1B_1 + c_1C_1$ where A_1, B_1, and C_1 are the CO-FACTORS of a_1, b_1 and c_1.

$$\triangle = a_1A_1 + b_1B_1 + c_1C_1$$

$$= a_1 \begin{vmatrix} b_2 & c_2 \\ b_3 & c_3 \end{vmatrix} - b_1 \begin{vmatrix} a_2 & c_2 \\ a_3 & c_3 \end{vmatrix} + c_1 \begin{vmatrix} a_2 & b_2 \\ a_3 & b_3 \end{vmatrix}$$

$$= a_1(b_2c_3 - b_3c_2) - b_1(a_2c_3 - a_3c_2) + c_1(a_2b_3 - a_3b_2)$$

$$= a_1b_2c_3 - a_1b_3c_2 - a_2b_1c_3 + a_3b_1c_2 + a_2b_3c_1 - a_3b_2c_1$$

$$= a_1b_2c_3 + a_2b_3c_1 + a_3b_1c_2 - a_1b_3c_2 - a_2b_1c_3 - a_3b_2c_1$$

There are three positive products and three negative products and it can be seen that they all have their factors lying along diagonals drawn through the array of elements.

$$\begin{vmatrix} a_1 & b_1 & c_1 \\ a_2 & b_2 & c_2 \\ a_3 & b_3 & c_3 \end{vmatrix} \begin{matrix} a_1 & b_1 \\ a_2 & b_2 \\ a_3 & b_3 \end{matrix}$$

$$-a_3b_2c_1 \quad -a_1b_3c_2 \quad -a_2b_1c_3 \qquad +a_1b_2c_3 \quad +a_3b_1c_2 \quad +a_2b_3c_1$$

This provides a rapid way to evaluate the positive and negative products—usually it can be done mentally. It is known as the RULE OF SARRUS *but is only applicable to third order determinants.*

Examples XVIII

1 Use the Rule of Sarrus to evaluate $\begin{vmatrix} 1 & 0 & 3 \\ 2 & 1 & 4 \\ 0 & 1 & 3 \end{vmatrix}$ and $\begin{vmatrix} 1 & 0 & 2 \\ 3 & 4 & 5 \\ 5 & 6 & 7 \end{vmatrix}$

and $\begin{vmatrix} 3 & 0 & 0 \\ 0 & 4 & 0 \\ 0 & 0 & 2 \end{vmatrix}$.

2 Find the determinants of the matrices $A = \begin{bmatrix} 1 & 0 & 0 \\ 2 & 3 & 5 \\ 4 & 1 & 3 \end{bmatrix}$ and

$B = \begin{bmatrix} 1 & 0 & 6 \\ 3 & 4 & 15 \\ 5 & 3 & 20 \end{bmatrix}$. Then multiply A and B and show that

$$|A.B| = |A|.|B|.$$

3 Is matrix $M = \begin{bmatrix} 0 & 2 & 3 \\ -2 & 0 & 4 \\ -3 & -4 & 0 \end{bmatrix}$ singular or non-singular?

4 If matrix $N = \begin{bmatrix} 2 & -2 & 2 \\ 1 & 3 & 2 \\ 2 & 44 & 3 \end{bmatrix}$ and $M = \begin{bmatrix} 0 & 2 & 3 \\ -2 & 0 & 4 \\ -3 & -4 & 0 \end{bmatrix}$ is the

product $N.M$ singular or non-singular?

87

5   Use the Rule of Sarrus to show that

$$\begin{vmatrix} a_1 & b_1 & (c_1+d_1) \\ a_2 & b_2 & (c_2+d_2) \\ a_3 & b_3 & (c_3+d_3) \end{vmatrix} = \begin{vmatrix} a_1 & b_1 & c_1 \\ a_2 & b_2 & c_2 \\ a_3 & b_3 & c_3 \end{vmatrix} + \begin{vmatrix} a_1 & b_1 & d_1 \\ a_2 & b_2 & d_2 \\ a_3 & b_3 & d_3 \end{vmatrix}$$

6   If $T = \begin{bmatrix} 1 & 0 & 0 \\ 3 & 1 & 0 \\ 4 & 2 & 1 \end{bmatrix}$, find det T, i.e. $|T|$, and $U = \begin{bmatrix} 1 & 5 & 7 \\ 0 & 1 & 3 \\ 0 & 0 & 1 \end{bmatrix}$,

find det U, i.e. $|U|$.

7   If $A = TU$ where T and U have the values of question 6 without calculation give $|A|$.

Reflections in Three Dimensions

The diagonal matrix $P = \begin{bmatrix} 1 & 0 & 0 \\ 0 & 1 & 0 \\ 0 & 0 & -1 \end{bmatrix}$.

When treating 2×2 matrices it was shown that the matrix $\begin{bmatrix} 1 & 0 \\ 0 & -1 \end{bmatrix}$ represents a reflection about the x axis. The matrix P above, is similar in form and if we examine the transformation of the matrix on a point T defined by (x, y, z) its image T' will be given by $\begin{bmatrix} 1 & 0 & 0 \\ 0 & 1 & 0 \\ 0 & 0 & -1 \end{bmatrix} \begin{bmatrix} x \\ y \\ z \end{bmatrix} = \begin{bmatrix} x' \\ y' \\ z' \end{bmatrix}$.

Multiplication gives

$$x' = x$$
$$y' = y$$
$$z' = -z$$

The image T' has the same ordinates in the xy plane but is obviously a *reflection in the xy plane*.

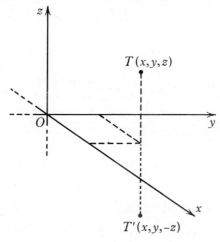

Diagram 26

The matrix $\begin{bmatrix} 1 & 0 & 0 \\ 0 & -1 & 0 \\ 0 & 0 & 1 \end{bmatrix}$ represents a reflection in the (x, z) plane.

The matrix $\begin{bmatrix} -1 & 0 & 0 \\ 0 & -1 & 0 \\ 0 & 0 & 1 \end{bmatrix}$ represents a reflection in the (y, z) plane followed by *another* reflection in the (x, z) plane.

It is obvious that *all* the possible reflections are included in the eight (3×3) matrices

$$\begin{bmatrix} 1 & 0 & 0 \\ 0 & 1 & 0 \\ 0 & 0 & 1 \end{bmatrix} \begin{bmatrix} 1 & 0 & 0 \\ 0 & 1 & 0 \\ 0 & 0 & -1 \end{bmatrix} \begin{bmatrix} 1 & 0 & 0 \\ 0 & -1 & 0 \\ 0 & 0 & 1 \end{bmatrix} \begin{bmatrix} -1 & 0 & 0 \\ 0 & 1 & 0 \\ 0 & 0 & 1 \end{bmatrix}$$

$$\begin{bmatrix} 1 & 0 & 0 \\ 0 & -1 & 0 \\ 0 & 0 & -1 \end{bmatrix} \begin{bmatrix} -1 & 0 & 0 \\ 0 & -1 & 0 \\ 0 & 0 & 1 \end{bmatrix} \begin{bmatrix} -1 & 0 & 0 \\ 0 & 1 & 0 \\ 0 & 0 & -1 \end{bmatrix} \begin{bmatrix} -1 & 0 & 0 \\ 0 & -1 & 0 \\ 0 & 0 & -1 \end{bmatrix}$$

The eight possible reflection matrices form a *group* of possible reflections in the three planes (x, y), (y, z), (x, z).

89

D

The matrix $\begin{bmatrix} 2 & 0 & 0 \\ 0 & 1 & 0 \\ 0 & 0 & -1 \end{bmatrix}$ therefore represents a reflection in

the (x, y) plane *and a stretch* of the x ordinate.

The matrix $\begin{bmatrix} 2 & 0 & 0 \\ 0 & 2 & 0 \\ 0 & 0 & -1 \end{bmatrix}$ would represent a reflection in the

(x, y) plane and a stretch in two directions in that plane.

The Diagonal Matrix

Some of the matrices studied so far, the Unit matrix $\begin{bmatrix} 1 & 0 & 0 \\ 0 & 1 & 0 \\ 0 & 0 & 1 \end{bmatrix}$,

the Scalar matrix $\begin{bmatrix} k & 0 & 0 \\ 0 & k & 0 \\ 0 & 0 & k \end{bmatrix} = kI$, and the Reflection matrices

are sub-groups of a very large and important group of matrices known as DIAGONAL matrices, of the form $\begin{bmatrix} \alpha & 0 & 0 \\ 0 & \beta & 0 \\ 0 & 0 & \gamma \end{bmatrix}$ where

α, β and γ are scalars. Using the method of expansion by CO-FACTORS or by using the *Rule of Sarrus*, it is obvious that the determinant of the diagonal matrix above is $\alpha\beta\gamma$. Since this is the general diagonal matrix, we can state in general terms that the determinant of a diagonal matrix is the scalar obtained by multiplying together the elements along the diagonal.

Diagonal matrices play a very important part in later work and require some special treatment.

Now take two different diagonal matrices

$$A = \begin{bmatrix} a_1 & 0 & 0 \\ 0 & b_1 & 0 \\ 0 & 0 & c_1 \end{bmatrix} \quad \text{and} \quad B = \begin{bmatrix} a_2 & 0 & 0 \\ 0 & b_2 & 0 \\ 0 & 0 & c_2 \end{bmatrix}$$

$$A.B = \begin{bmatrix} a_1 & 0 & 0 \\ 0 & b_1 & 0 \\ 0 & 0 & c_1 \end{bmatrix} \begin{bmatrix} a_2 & 0 & 0 \\ 0 & b_2 & 0 \\ 0 & 0 & c_2 \end{bmatrix} = \begin{bmatrix} a_1 a_2 & 0 & 0 \\ 0 & b_1 b_2 & 0 \\ 0 & 0 & c_1 c_2 \end{bmatrix}$$

also

$$B.A = \begin{bmatrix} a_2 & 0 & 0 \\ 0 & b_2 & 0 \\ 0 & 0 & c_2 \end{bmatrix} \begin{bmatrix} a_1 & 0 & 0 \\ 0 & b_1 & 0 \\ 0 & 0 & c_1 \end{bmatrix} = \begin{bmatrix} a_2 a_1 & 0 & 0 \\ 0 & b_2 b_1 & 0 \\ 0 & 0 & c_2 c_1 \end{bmatrix}$$

Hence these two diagonal matrices commute

$$A.B = B.A$$

and the product is also a diagonal matrix. We induce that $A.B.C = C.B.A$ if C is a diagonal matrix the product must be another diagonal matrix.

It follows too that if $A = B$ then

$$A^2 = \begin{bmatrix} a_1^2 & 0 & 0 \\ 0 & b_1^2 & 0 \\ 0 & 0 & c_1^2 \end{bmatrix} \qquad A^3 = \begin{bmatrix} a_1^3 & 0 & 0 \\ 0 & b_1^3 & 0 \\ 0 & 0 & c_1^3 \end{bmatrix}$$

and hence

$$A^n = \begin{bmatrix} a_1^n & 0 & 0 \\ 0 & b_1^n & 0 \\ 0 & 0 & c_1^n \end{bmatrix}$$

Diagonal matrices are very simple to use and because of their simplicity are useful in many applications. The inverse is simple to find.

$$|A| = a_1 b_1 c_1 \qquad A^{-1} = \frac{1}{a_1 b_1 c_1} \begin{bmatrix} b_1 c_1 & 0 & 0 \\ 0 & a_1 c_1 & 0 \\ 0 & 0 & a_1 b_1 \end{bmatrix}$$

$$= \begin{bmatrix} a^{-1} & 0 & 0 \\ 0 & b^{-1} & 0 \\ 0 & 0 & c^{-1} \end{bmatrix}$$

This latter result is easy to remember.

91

Triangular (3×3) Matrices

Triangular (3×3) matrices have properties similar to those of (2×2) matrices. If $A = \begin{bmatrix} a_1 & b_1 & c_1 \\ a_2 & b_2 & c_2 \\ a_3 & b_3 & c_3 \end{bmatrix}$ and $T = \begin{bmatrix} 1 & 1 & 0 \\ 0 & 1 & 0 \\ 0 & 0 & 1 \end{bmatrix}$, T is a

triangular matrix because the elements below the leading diagonal are all zeros.

$$T.A = \begin{bmatrix} 1 & 1 & 0 \\ 0 & 1 & 0 \\ 0 & 0 & 1 \end{bmatrix} \begin{bmatrix} a_1 & b_1 & c_1 \\ a_2 & b_2 & c_2 \\ a_3 & b_3 & c_3 \end{bmatrix} = \begin{bmatrix} a_1+a_2 & b_1+b_2 & c_1+c_2 \\ a_2 & b_2 & c_2 \\ a_3 & b_3 & c_3 \end{bmatrix}$$

Pre-multiplication of A by T has been equivalent to the addition of *row* 2 to *row* 1.

$$A.T = \begin{bmatrix} a_1 & b_1 & c_1 \\ a_2 & b_2 & c_2 \\ a_3 & b_3 & c_3 \end{bmatrix} \begin{bmatrix} 1 & 1 & 0 \\ 0 & 1 & 0 \\ 0 & 0 & 1 \end{bmatrix} = \begin{bmatrix} a_1 & a_1+b_1 & c_1 \\ a_2 & a_2+b_2 & c_2 \\ a_3 & a_3+b_3 & c_3 \end{bmatrix}$$

Post-multiplication of A by T has caused the addition of *column* 1 to *column* 2.

$$\text{If } T_1 = \begin{bmatrix} 1 & 0 & 3 \\ 0 & 1 & 0 \\ 0 & 0 & 1 \end{bmatrix} \text{ then } T_1 A = \begin{bmatrix} 1 & 0 & 3 \\ 0 & 1 & 0 \\ 0 & 0 & 1 \end{bmatrix} \begin{bmatrix} a_1 & b_1 & c_1 \\ a_2 & b_2 & c_2 \\ a_3 & b_3 & c_3 \end{bmatrix}$$

$$= \begin{bmatrix} a_1+3a_3 & b_1+3b_3 & c_1+3c_3 \\ a_2 & b_2 & c_2 \\ a_3 & b_3 & c_3 \end{bmatrix}$$

The matrix T_1 has resulted in the addition of three times the third row to the first row.

We can state that *pre-multiplication* by a *suitable* triangular matrix causes the addition (or subtraction) of one row (or a scalar multiple of that row) to another row. *Post-multiplication* has the same effect on columns.

If $N = \begin{bmatrix} 0 & 1 & 0 \\ 1 & 0 & 0 \\ 0 & 0 & 1 \end{bmatrix}$ and as before $A = \begin{bmatrix} a_1 & b_1 & c_1 \\ a_2 & b_2 & c_2 \\ a_3 & b_3 & c_3 \end{bmatrix}$ then

$$N.A = \begin{bmatrix} 0 & 1 & 0 \\ 1 & 0 & 0 \\ 0 & 0 & 1 \end{bmatrix} \begin{bmatrix} a_1 & b_1 & c_1 \\ a_2 & b_2 & c_2 \\ a_3 & b_3 & c_3 \end{bmatrix} = \begin{bmatrix} a_2 & b_2 & c_2 \\ a_1 & b_1 & c_1 \\ a_3 & b_3 & c_3 \end{bmatrix}$$

Pre-multiplication by N has interchanged row 2 and row 1 of matrix A. (Post-multiplication would have interchanged column 1 and column 2.)

The diagonal matrix $M = \begin{bmatrix} 1 & 0 & 0 \\ 0 & 3 & 0 \\ 0 & 0 & 2 \end{bmatrix}$ would give a result as follows:

$$M.A = \begin{bmatrix} 1 & 0 & 0 \\ 0 & 3 & 0 \\ 0 & 0 & 2 \end{bmatrix} \begin{bmatrix} a_1 & b_1 & c_1 \\ a_2 & b_2 & c_2 \\ a_3 & b_3 & c_3 \end{bmatrix} = \begin{bmatrix} a_1 & b_1 & c_1 \\ 3a_2 & 3b_2 & 3c_2 \\ 2a_3 & 2b_3 & 2c_3 \end{bmatrix}$$

The second row has been multiplied by 3 and the third row by 2.

Examples XIX

1 $A = \begin{bmatrix} 3 & -1 & 2 \\ 1 & 1 & 0 \\ 2 & -2 & 0 \end{bmatrix}$, $D = \begin{bmatrix} 2 & 0 & 0 \\ 0 & 3 & 0 \\ 0 & 0 & -2 \end{bmatrix}$, find AD and DA.

2 $B = \begin{bmatrix} 1 & 2 & 3 \\ 2 & 0 & 4 \\ 1 & 2 & 6 \end{bmatrix}$, $D = \begin{bmatrix} 1 & 0 & 0 \\ 0 & 4 & 0 \\ 0 & 0 & 7 \end{bmatrix}$, find BD and DB.

3 $E = \begin{bmatrix} 1 & 0 & 0 \\ 0 & -1 & 0 \\ 0 & 0 & 3 \end{bmatrix}$, $F = \begin{bmatrix} 3 & 0 & 0 \\ 0 & 2 & 0 \\ 0 & 0 & -1 \end{bmatrix}$, find $|E|$, $|F|$, $|EF|$.

4 $G = \begin{bmatrix} 2 & 0 & 0 \\ 0 & -2 & 0 \\ 0 & 0 & 3 \end{bmatrix}$, find $|G|$, $|G^2|$, $|3G|$.

5 $B = \begin{bmatrix} 3 & -1 & 2 \\ 1 & 1 & 2 \\ 3 & -2 & 0 \end{bmatrix}$, $T = \begin{bmatrix} 1 & 1 & 0 \\ 0 & 1 & 0 \\ 0 & 0 & 1 \end{bmatrix}$, find BT and TB,

then find $|B|$, $|T|$, $|BT|$, $|TB|$.

6 $T = \begin{bmatrix} 1 & 1 & 0 \\ 0 & 1 & 0 \\ 0 & 0 & 1 \end{bmatrix}$, $V = \begin{bmatrix} 1 & 0 & 0 \\ 1 & 1 & 0 \\ 0 & 0 & 1 \end{bmatrix}$, find TV, VT, V^2, T^2.

7 $L = \begin{bmatrix} 1 & 0 & 0 \\ a & 1 & 0 \\ b & c & 1 \end{bmatrix}$, $U = \begin{bmatrix} 1 & d & e \\ 0 & 1 & f \\ 0 & 0 & 1 \end{bmatrix}$, find the matrix A such that

$A = LU$. To which class of matrices do L and U belong?

8 If in question 7, $A = \begin{bmatrix} 1 & 2 & 2 \\ 2 & 5 & 8 \\ 3 & 7 & 11 \end{bmatrix}$, find the values of a, b, c, d, e, f

in L and U. Express A as the product of two triangular matrices.

9 Find the inverse of matrix L in question 8.

10 Find $|L|$ and $|U|$ for the matrices of question 8.

The Elementary Transformations

We have shown that three ELEMENTARY TRANSFORMATIONS of a matrix can be brought about by pre-multiplication or post-multiplication by another *suitable* matrix.

Definition

The ELEMENTARY TRANSFORMATIONS of a matrix are
  (i) the interchange of two rows (or columns)

(ii) the multiplication of each element of a row (or column) by scalar

(iii) the addition of a scalar multiple of one row (or column) to another row.

   If matrix A can be transformed by one of these elementary transformations into matrix B, then A is said to be EQUIVALENT to B. (Shown $A \sim B$.) The elementary transformations can be used to find the inverse of a matrix.

Finding the Inverse Matrix using the Elementary Transformations

The work is carried out in two parallel columns and since each transformation is the result of multiplying by a suitable matrix, each matrix operation can be represented by a different letter. *Pre-multiplication* causing *row operations* will be used on the unit matrix also.

$$A = \begin{bmatrix} 1 & 2 & 1 \\ 2 & 4 & 6 \\ 3 & 1 & 2 \end{bmatrix} \qquad I = \begin{bmatrix} 1 & 0 & 0 \\ 0 & 1 & 0 \\ 0 & 0 & 1 \end{bmatrix}$$

Subtract twice row 1 from row 2. This is equivalent to pre-multiplication by some matrix P.

   Both matrix A and matrix I are subjected to the *same* matrix operation on each occasion.

$$PA = \begin{bmatrix} 1 & 2 & 1 \\ 0 & 0 & 4 \\ 3 & 1 & 2 \end{bmatrix} \qquad PI = \begin{bmatrix} 1 & 0 & 0 \\ -2 & 1 & 0 \\ 0 & 0 & 1 \end{bmatrix}$$

Subtract $3 \times$ row 1 from row 3

$$QPA = \begin{bmatrix} 1 & 2 & 1 \\ 0 & 0 & 4 \\ 0 & -5 & -1 \end{bmatrix} \qquad QPI = \begin{bmatrix} 1 & 0 & 0 \\ -2 & 1 & 0 \\ -3 & 0 & 1 \end{bmatrix}$$

Introduction to Matrices

Add row 3 to row 1

$$RQPA = \begin{bmatrix} 1 & -3 & 0 \\ 0 & 0 & 4 \\ 0 & -5 & -1 \end{bmatrix} \qquad RQPI = \begin{bmatrix} -2 & 0 & 1 \\ -2 & 1 & 0 \\ -3 & 0 & 1 \end{bmatrix}$$

Add $4 \times$ row 3 to row 1

$$SRQPA = \begin{bmatrix} 1 & -3 & 0 \\ 0 & -20 & 0 \\ 0 & -5 & -1 \end{bmatrix} \qquad SRQPI = \begin{bmatrix} -2 & 0 & 1 \\ -14 & 1 & 4 \\ -3 & 0 & 1 \end{bmatrix}$$

Subtract $\frac{1}{4} \times$ row 2 from row 3

$$TSRQPA = \begin{bmatrix} 1 & -3 & 0 \\ 0 & -20 & 0 \\ 0 & 0 & -1 \end{bmatrix} \qquad TSRQPI = \begin{bmatrix} -2 & 0 & 1 \\ -14 & 1 & 4 \\ \frac{1}{2} & -\frac{1}{4} & 0 \end{bmatrix}$$

Divide row 2 by -20 and row 3 by -1

$$UTSRQPA = \begin{bmatrix} 1 & -3 & 0 \\ 0 & 1 & 0 \\ 0 & 0 & 1 \end{bmatrix} \qquad UTSRQPI = \begin{bmatrix} -2 & 0 & 1 \\ \frac{7}{10} & \frac{-1}{20} & \frac{-5}{5} \\ -\frac{1}{2} & \frac{1}{4} & 0 \end{bmatrix}$$

Add $3 \times$ row 2 to row 1

$$WUTSRQPA = \begin{bmatrix} 1 & 0 & 0 \\ 0 & 1 & 0 \\ 0 & 0 & 1 \end{bmatrix} \qquad WUTSRQPI = \begin{bmatrix} \frac{1}{10} & \frac{-3}{20} & \frac{2}{5} \\ \frac{7}{10} & \frac{-1}{20} & \frac{1}{5} \\ -\frac{1}{2} & \frac{1}{4} & 0 \end{bmatrix}$$

In column 1 the matrix A has been transformed to the unit matrix

$$(WUTSRQP).A = I$$

$$\Rightarrow (WUTSRQP) = A^{-1}$$

But in the second column we have $(WUTSRQP).I = A^{-1}I = A^{-1}$. Thus the matrix in column 2 is the inverse matrix A^{-1}.

$$A^{-1} = \begin{bmatrix} \dfrac{1}{10} & \dfrac{-3}{20} & \dfrac{2}{5} \\ \dfrac{7}{10} & \dfrac{-1}{20} & \dfrac{-1}{5} \\ \dfrac{-1}{2} & \dfrac{1}{4} & 0 \end{bmatrix} = \dfrac{1}{20} \begin{bmatrix} 2 & -3 & 8 \\ 14 & -1 & -4 \\ -10 & 5 & 0 \end{bmatrix}$$

The process has been set out in full, since the operations are simple many of them can be carried out in a single operation and the result then follows quickly. It must be emphasized that row operations only have been used, i.e. pre-multiplication.

Although we have illustrated the elementary transformations using (3×3) matrices, they can be extended to other groups of matrices.

Further applications of the elementary transformations arise in later work.

For finding the inverse of matrices larger than (3×3) this method is more efficient than any other method using determinants.

Examples XX

1 Using elementary transformation *by rows* reduce $\begin{bmatrix} 3 & 4 \\ 2 & 3 \end{bmatrix}$ to the inverse matrix and check.

2 Find the determinant of $\begin{bmatrix} -2 & 3 \\ 4 & -7 \end{bmatrix}$ and then reduce to the inverse matrix using row transformations.

3 Using elementary row transformations find the inverse of $\begin{bmatrix} 2 & 1 & 1 \\ 1 & 2 & 2 \\ 1 & 3 & 2 \end{bmatrix}$. Check your result.

4 $A = \begin{bmatrix} 1 & 0 & 3 \\ 2 & 1 & 4 \\ 0 & 1 & 3 \end{bmatrix}$, find A^{-1}.

5 $Q = \begin{bmatrix} 3 & 2 & 1 \\ 4 & 2 & 2 \\ 1 & 3 & 0 \end{bmatrix}$, find Q^{-1}.

6 $R = \begin{bmatrix} 0 & 0 & 1 \\ 0 & 1 & 0 \\ 1 & 0 & 0 \end{bmatrix}$, find R^{-1}.

Applications of Matrix Algebra

Matrix Algebra is one of the great developments of nineteenth-century mathematics but it is only in recent times that its application in so many different fields has been realized. The rapid growth of Linear Programming since 1947 has emphasized the need for matrix methods in this new branch of mathematics. More recently the application of matrix algebra has given the electrical engineer a powerful method in the analysis of electrical networks.

The use of matrix methods in electronics, quantum theory, newer branches of social science, aerodynamics, theory of vibrations, physical chemistry, higher mathematics and above all in modern computer techniques, makes certain concepts of matrix algebra essential for the understanding of these applications. Of outstanding importance for this purpose is the study of Eigenvalues and Characteristic Function, Linear Dependence and Rank. Because of their wide applications these and other topics will be dealt with at appropriate places in the succeeding chapters.

Latent Roots, Eigenvalues and Characteristic Equation

The (2×2) matrix $A = \begin{bmatrix} 2 & 4 \\ 3 & 13 \end{bmatrix}$ represents a transformation in two-dimensional space.

So a vector $\begin{bmatrix} x \\ y \end{bmatrix}$ is transformed to $\begin{bmatrix} x' \\ y' \end{bmatrix}$, i.e. $A . \begin{bmatrix} x \\ y \end{bmatrix} = \begin{bmatrix} x' \\ y' \end{bmatrix}$.

If the transformed vector $\begin{bmatrix} x' \\ y' \end{bmatrix}$ has the *same direction* as the original vector $\begin{bmatrix} x \\ y \end{bmatrix}$ then we have shown earlier that it can be represented by

$\begin{bmatrix} \lambda x \\ \lambda y \end{bmatrix}$ or $\lambda \begin{bmatrix} x \\ y \end{bmatrix}$. Such a vector is called a CHARACTERISTIC VECTOR (or, EIGENVECTOR) of the matrix A.

In the case of the (2×2) matrix there are not more than *two* values of λ possible. The values of λ are called the CHARACTERISTIC ROOTS or LATENT ROOTS or EIGENVALUES of the matrix. We shall also show that there are not more than three characteristic roots for a (3×3) matrix and so on.

If we use X to denote the vector then $A . X = \lambda X$ for the condition understood, and since $\lambda X = \lambda I X$ where I is the Unit Matrix then

$$AX = \lambda IX$$

$$(A - \lambda I) . X = 0 \qquad \ldots \text{(i)}$$

The determinant of the R.H.S. is zero, therefore one of the two matrices $(A - \lambda I)$ or X must be singular and since X is a vector then $(A - \lambda I)$ must be singular, i.e. its determinant is zero.

$$|A - \lambda I| = 0$$

This is called the CHARACTERISTIC EQUATION of the matrix A. $|(A - \lambda I)|$ is called the CHARACTERISTIC FUNCTION of A.

The solution of $|A - \lambda I| = 0$ gives the latent roots or eigenvalues. Substituting the known values of the elements of A gives

$$\left| \begin{bmatrix} 2 & 4 \\ 3 & 13 \end{bmatrix} - \begin{bmatrix} \lambda & 0 \\ 0 & \lambda \end{bmatrix} \right| = 0$$

$$\Rightarrow \begin{vmatrix} 2 - \lambda & 4 \\ 3 & 13 - \lambda \end{vmatrix} = 0$$

$$\Rightarrow (2-\lambda)(13-\lambda)-12 = 0$$

$$\Rightarrow \lambda^2 - 15\lambda + 14 = 0$$

$$\Rightarrow (\lambda - 14)(\lambda - 1) = 0$$

$$\Rightarrow \lambda = 14 \quad \text{or} \quad 1$$

Substituting these values for λ in the equation shown at (i) gives

$$\left[\begin{bmatrix} 2 & 4 \\ 3 & 13 \end{bmatrix} - \begin{bmatrix} 14 & 0 \\ 0 & 14 \end{bmatrix}\right] X = 0$$

$$\begin{bmatrix} -12 & 4 \\ 3 & -1 \end{bmatrix} X = 0$$

If vector X is $\begin{bmatrix} x \\ y \end{bmatrix}$

then

$$\begin{bmatrix} -12 & 4 \\ 3 & -1 \end{bmatrix}\begin{bmatrix} x \\ y \end{bmatrix} = 0$$

$$\Rightarrow \left.\begin{array}{c} -12x + 4y = 0 \\ 3x - y = 0 \end{array}\right\} \quad \left.\begin{array}{l} x = 1 \\ y = 3 \end{array}\right\} \text{is an obvious root}$$

and

For $\lambda = 1$ the relation becomes $\begin{bmatrix} 2-1 & 4 \\ 3 & 13-1 \end{bmatrix}\begin{bmatrix} x \\ y \end{bmatrix} = 0$

$$\left.\begin{array}{c} \Rightarrow x + 4y = 0 \\ 3x + 12y = 0 \end{array}\right. \quad \text{and} \quad \left.\begin{array}{l} x = 4 \\ y = -1 \end{array}\right\} \text{satisfies these equations}$$

The two vectors $\begin{bmatrix} 1 \\ 3 \end{bmatrix}$ and $\begin{bmatrix} 4 \\ -1 \end{bmatrix}$ are the eigenvectors of the matrix A.

Any vector of the form $k\begin{bmatrix} 1 \\ 3 \end{bmatrix}$ or $k'\begin{bmatrix} 4 \\ -1 \end{bmatrix}$, where k and k' are any real numbers, would also satisfy the relation $(A - \lambda I)X = 0$. So finally we state that any vectors whose elements are in the ratio of $1:3$ or $4:-1$ are eigenvectors of the matrix A.

100

Next we apply the transformation A to them

$$\begin{bmatrix} 2 & 4 \\ 3 & 13 \end{bmatrix}\begin{bmatrix} 1 \\ 3 \end{bmatrix} = \begin{bmatrix} x^1 \\ y' \end{bmatrix} \Rightarrow \begin{matrix} x' = 14 \\ y' = 42 \end{matrix} = 14\begin{bmatrix} 1 \\ 3 \end{bmatrix}$$

$$\begin{bmatrix} 2 & 4 \\ 3 & 13 \end{bmatrix}\begin{bmatrix} 4 \\ -1 \end{bmatrix} = \begin{bmatrix} x'' \\ y'' \end{bmatrix} \Rightarrow \begin{matrix} x'' = 4 \\ y'' = -1 \end{matrix} = 1\begin{bmatrix} 4 \\ -1 \end{bmatrix}$$

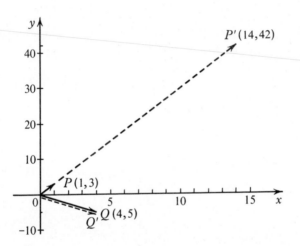

Diagram 27

The vector OP has transformed to OP' in the *same* direction but 14 times magnified in the first case and magnified by 1 in the second case when OQ transforms to OQ' in the *same* direction.

Any vectors of the form $k\begin{bmatrix} 1 \\ 3 \end{bmatrix}$ or $k'\begin{bmatrix} 4 \\ -1 \end{bmatrix}$ will be transformed by the matrix A in the *same* direction. No vectors of 2 dimensions in any other direction will be transformed by matrix A in the same direction.

We have given a geometrical illustration of the *eigenvectors* of the matrix $A = \begin{bmatrix} 2 & 4 \\ 3 & 13 \end{bmatrix}$.

101

Reduction of a Matrix to Diagonal Form

The matrix constructed from the two eigenvectors $\begin{bmatrix} 1 \\ 3 \end{bmatrix}$ and $\begin{bmatrix} 4 \\ -1 \end{bmatrix}$

has important and useful applications. Let this matrix be $Q = \begin{bmatrix} 1 & 4 \\ 3 & -1 \end{bmatrix}$, its inverse

$$Q^{-1} = \frac{-1}{13} \begin{bmatrix} -1 & -4 \\ -3 & 1 \end{bmatrix}.$$

It can be proved that if the original matrix A is pre-multiplied by Q^{-1} and post-multiplied by Q the new matrix will be a DIAGONAL matrix, call it N

$$N = Q^{-1}AQ = \frac{-1}{13} \begin{bmatrix} -1 & -4 \\ -3 & 1 \end{bmatrix}\begin{bmatrix} 2 & 4 \\ 3 & 13 \end{bmatrix}\begin{bmatrix} 1 & 4 \\ 3 & -1 \end{bmatrix}$$

$$= \frac{-1}{13} \begin{bmatrix} -1 & -4 \\ -3 & 1 \end{bmatrix}\begin{bmatrix} 14 & 4 \\ 42 & -1 \end{bmatrix}$$

$$= \frac{-1}{13} \begin{bmatrix} -182 & 0 \\ 0 & -13 \end{bmatrix}$$

$$= \begin{bmatrix} 14 & 0 \\ 0 & 1 \end{bmatrix}$$

Note that the elements along the diagonal are the original roots of the characteristic equation of matrix A.

Examples XXI

1 Write down the characteristic equation and solve for the latent roots (or eigenroots or eigenvalues) of $A = \begin{bmatrix} -15 & -12 \\ 24 & 19 \end{bmatrix}$.

2 Write down the characteristic equation and find the latent roots (or eigenroots) of $B = \begin{bmatrix} 3 & -1 \\ 0 & 4 \end{bmatrix}$.

3 Find the latent roots of $C = \begin{bmatrix} 17 & 24 \\ -12 & -17 \end{bmatrix}$.

4 Find the eigenvectors of matrix A in question 1.

5 Form the matrix Q with the eigenvectors of question 4, find its inverse and hence find the diagonal matrix equivalent to matrix A of question 1.

6 Reduce matrix $B = \begin{bmatrix} 3 & -1 \\ 0 & 4 \end{bmatrix}$ to diagonal form.

Latent Roots and Eigen Vectors of a (3 × 3) Matrix

To find the latent roots and eigenvectors of the (3×3) matrix $B = \begin{bmatrix} 0 & -1 & -2 \\ 2 & 3 & 2 \\ 1 & 1 & 3 \end{bmatrix}$.

The characteristic equation is $|B - \lambda I| = 0$, from which the latent roots can be calculated:

$$\left| \begin{bmatrix} 0 & -1 & -2 \\ 2 & 3 & 2 \\ 1 & 1 & 3 \end{bmatrix} - \begin{bmatrix} \lambda & 0 & 0 \\ 0 & \lambda & 0 \\ 0 & 0 & \lambda \end{bmatrix} \right| = 0$$

$$\Rightarrow \begin{vmatrix} (0-\lambda) & -1 & -2 \\ 2 & (3-\lambda) & 2 \\ 1 & 1 & (3-\lambda) \end{vmatrix} = 0$$

$$\Rightarrow \lambda^3 - 6\lambda^2 + 11\lambda - 6 = 0$$
$$\Rightarrow (\lambda - 1)(\lambda - 2)(\lambda - 3) = 0$$
$$\Rightarrow \lambda = 1 \quad \text{or} \quad 2 \quad \text{or} \quad 3$$

The latent roots of matrix B are $+1$, $+2$, and $+3$.
Substituting these roots in turn in the matrix relations

$$[B-(1)I]\begin{bmatrix} x \\ y \\ z \end{bmatrix} = 0, \; [B-(2)I]\begin{bmatrix} x \\ y \\ z \end{bmatrix} = 0, \; [B-(3)I]\begin{bmatrix} x \\ y \\ z \end{bmatrix} = 0$$

gives

(i)
$$\begin{bmatrix} -1 & -1 & -2 \\ 2 & 2 & 2 \\ 1 & 1 & 2 \end{bmatrix}\begin{bmatrix} x \\ y \\ z \end{bmatrix} = 0$$

$$\Rightarrow \quad -x - y - 2z = 0$$
$$2x + 2y + z = 0$$
$$x + y + 2z = 0$$
$$\Rightarrow \quad x = 1, \ y = -1, \ z = 0$$

The eigenvector corresponding to the root $+1$ is $\begin{bmatrix} 1 \\ -1 \\ 0 \end{bmatrix}$

(ii)
$$\begin{bmatrix} -2 & -1 & -2 \\ 2 & 1 & 2 \\ 1 & 1 & 1 \end{bmatrix}\begin{bmatrix} x \\ y \\ z \end{bmatrix} = 0 \qquad \text{(for root } \lambda = +2)$$

$$\Rightarrow \quad 2x + y + 2z = 0$$
$$2x + y + 2z = 0$$
$$x + y + z = 0$$
$$y = 0, \quad x = +1, \quad z = -1$$

The eigenvector corresponding to root $+2$ is $\begin{bmatrix} 1 \\ 0 \\ -1 \end{bmatrix}$.

(iii)
$$\begin{bmatrix} -3 & -1 & -2 \\ 2 & 0 & 2 \\ 1 & 1 & 0 \end{bmatrix}\begin{bmatrix} x \\ y \\ z \end{bmatrix} = 0 \qquad \text{(for root } \lambda = +3)$$

$$3x + y + 2z = 0$$
$$2x + 2z = 0$$
$$x + y = 0$$
$$x = 1, \quad y = -1, \quad z = -1$$

The eigenvector corresponding to root $+3$ is $\begin{bmatrix} 1 \\ 1 \\ -1 \end{bmatrix}$

The matrix Q formed from these three eigenvectors is

$$Q = \begin{bmatrix} 1 & 1 & 1 \\ -1 & 0 & -1 \\ 0 & -1 & -1 \end{bmatrix}$$

and if the inverse of Q is calculated, it is found to be

$$Q^{-1} = -1 \begin{bmatrix} -1 & 0 & -1 \\ -1 & -1 & 0 \\ 1 & 1 & 1 \end{bmatrix}.$$

Then

$$Q^{-1}BQ = -1 \begin{bmatrix} -1 & 0 & -1 \\ -1 & -1 & 0 \\ 1 & 1 & 1 \end{bmatrix} \begin{bmatrix} 0 & -1 & -2 \\ 2 & 3 & 2 \\ 1 & 1 & 3 \end{bmatrix} \begin{bmatrix} 1 & 1 & 1 \\ -1 & 0 & -1 \\ 0 & -1 & -1 \end{bmatrix}$$

$$= -1 \begin{bmatrix} -1 & 0 & -1 \\ -1 & -1 & 0 \\ 1 & 1 & 1 \end{bmatrix} \begin{bmatrix} 1 & 2 & 3 \\ -1 & 0 & -3 \\ 0 & -2 & -3 \end{bmatrix}$$

$$= -1 \begin{bmatrix} -1 & 0 & 0 \\ 0 & -2 & 0 \\ 0 & 0 & -3 \end{bmatrix}$$

$$= \begin{bmatrix} 1 & 0 & 0 \\ 0 & 2 & 0 \\ 0 & 0 & 3 \end{bmatrix} = M$$

The operation has produced a diagonal matrix with the three eigenroots (or latent roots) of B as elements along the leading diagonal.

Examples XXII

1   If $A = \begin{bmatrix} -2 & -3 & -1 \\ 1 & 2 & 1 \\ 3 & 3 & 2 \end{bmatrix}$ write down the characteristic equation

and solve for the latent roots.

2   Find the eigenvectors for the matrix A above and hence reduce A to diagonal form.

3   If $B = \begin{bmatrix} 1 & -1 & -2 \\ 2 & 4 & 2 \\ 1 & 1 & 4 \end{bmatrix}$ write down the characteristic equation

and solve for the latent roots.

4   Find the eigenvectors for the matrix B in question 3 and hence reduce B to diagonal form.

Section IV

Rectangular Matrices

The treatment of matrices so far has been confined to (2×2) and (3×3) matrices and the use of the column matrix to represent a mathematical quantity, i.e. a vector. When the number of columns and rows are equal, the matrix is said to be SQUARE and the treatment of square matrices forms the greater proportion of the subject at this level, but other matrices, with the number of columns *not* equal to the number of rows, called RECTANGULAR matrices, must receive some consideration. They often arise in the treatment of linear equations.

$$y' = a_1 x_1 + b_1 x_2 + c_1 x_3$$
$$y'' = a_2 x_1 + b_2 x_2 + c_2 x_3$$

In matrix form this becomes

$$\begin{bmatrix} y' \\ y'' \end{bmatrix} = \begin{bmatrix} a_1 & b_1 & c_1 \\ a_2 & b_2 & c_2 \end{bmatrix} \begin{bmatrix} x_1 \\ x_2 \\ x_3 \end{bmatrix}$$

The matrix $\begin{bmatrix} a_1 & b_1 & c_1 \\ a_2 & b_2 & c_2 \end{bmatrix}$ has three columns but only two rows, it is called a (2×3) rectangular matrix. (*Note:* Rows are always given first, columns second.)

The product of the (2×3) matrix with the (3×1) column matrix yields a (2×1) column matrix. Inspection shows that two matrices can be added only if they have the same number of rows and columns, i.e. they are said to be CONFORMABLE for addition.

Two matrices can be multiplied together *only if* the number of columns of the first is the same as the number of rows of the second, and again they are said to be CONFORMABLE for multiplication.

For matrices which are *not* square (i.e. rectangular) it is impossible to define a determinant or an inverse.

107

Introduction to Matrices

Example (i)

Add $A = \begin{bmatrix} 1 & 3 & -1 & 2 \\ 3 & 2 & 2 & 0 \\ 1 & 3 & 5 & -2 \end{bmatrix}$ to $B = \begin{bmatrix} 1 & 1 & 0 & 2 \\ 2 & 1 & 0 & 3 \\ 0 & 4 & -1 & 3 \end{bmatrix}$

$$A + B = \begin{bmatrix} 2 & 4 & -1 & 4 \\ 5 & 3 & 2 & 3 \\ 1 & 7 & 4 & 1 \end{bmatrix}$$

Example (ii)

Multiply $C = \begin{bmatrix} 1 & 4 & 2 \\ -1 & 3 & 1 \end{bmatrix}$ by $D = \begin{bmatrix} 2 & -1 \\ 4 & 3 \\ 2 & 5 \end{bmatrix}$

$$C.D = \begin{bmatrix} 1 & 4 & 2 \\ -1 & 3 & 1 \end{bmatrix} \begin{bmatrix} 2 & -1 \\ 4 & 3 \\ 2 & 5 \end{bmatrix}$$

$$= \begin{bmatrix} \begin{pmatrix} 1 \times 2 \\ 4 \times 4 \\ 2 \times 2 \end{pmatrix} & \begin{pmatrix} 1 \times -1 \\ 4 \times 3 \\ 2 \times 5 \end{pmatrix} \\ \begin{pmatrix} -1 \times 2 \\ 3 \times 4 \\ 1 \times 2 \end{pmatrix} & \begin{pmatrix} -1 \times -1 \\ 3 \times 3 \\ 1 \times 5 \end{pmatrix} \end{bmatrix}$$

$$= \begin{bmatrix} (2+16+4) & (-1+12+10) \\ (-2+12+2) & (1+9+5) \end{bmatrix} = \begin{bmatrix} 22 & 21 \\ 12 & 15 \end{bmatrix}$$

C is a (2×3) matrix, D is (3×2) matrix, and the product is a (2×2) matrix.

Examples XXIII

$$A = \begin{bmatrix} 2 & 3 & -1 & 2 \\ 3 & 4 & 6 & 1 \end{bmatrix} \quad B = \begin{bmatrix} 6 & 3 \\ 2 & 1 \end{bmatrix} \quad C = \begin{bmatrix} 4 & 0 & 2 & 1 \\ -1 & 6 & 3 & 8 \end{bmatrix}$$

$$D = \begin{bmatrix} 2 & 3 \\ 4 & 1 \\ 6 & 8 \\ 9 & 2 \end{bmatrix} \quad E = \begin{bmatrix} 2 & 1 & 0 & 3 \\ 3 & 2 & 1 & 6 \\ -1 & 2 & 0 & 0 \\ 4 & 3 & 1 & 2 \end{bmatrix} \quad F = \begin{bmatrix} 2 & 1 & 2 \\ 3 & 0 & 6 \\ 2 & 1 & 8 \\ 4 & 1 & 6 \end{bmatrix}$$

$$G = \begin{bmatrix} 2 & 1 & 6 \\ 4 & 1 & 2 \\ 1 & -1 & 2 \end{bmatrix}$$

1 Describe *A*, *B*, *C*, *D*, *E*, *F* and *G* as $(n \times m)$ matrices. (*Hint*: *A* is a 2×4 matrix.)

2 State which matrices are conformable for addition and give the sums.

3 State which matrices are conformable for multiplication and give the products and class of matrix $(n \times m)$ involved.

4 Expand

$$\begin{bmatrix} x' \\ y' \end{bmatrix} = \begin{bmatrix} 1 & 0 & 3 \\ 0 & 1 & 4 \end{bmatrix} \begin{bmatrix} x \\ y \\ 1 \end{bmatrix}$$

and state the kind of geometrical transformation it represents.

5 What kind of transformations are represented by

$$\begin{bmatrix} x' \\ y' \end{bmatrix} = \begin{bmatrix} 1 & 0 & 3 \\ 0 & -1 & -4 \end{bmatrix} \begin{bmatrix} x \\ y \\ 1 \end{bmatrix}$$

(2×2) Matrices and Quadratic Forms

The transpose of a column matrix is a row matrix.

If $A = \begin{bmatrix} x \\ y \end{bmatrix}$ then $A^t = [x \quad y]$

$$A^t . A = [x \quad y] \begin{bmatrix} x \\ y \end{bmatrix} = x^2 + y^2$$

109

Next we examine the matrix product which uses this property:

$$[x \quad y]\begin{bmatrix} 5 & 2 \\ 2 & 3 \end{bmatrix}\begin{bmatrix} x \\ y \end{bmatrix} = [x \quad y]\begin{bmatrix} (5x+2y) \\ (2x+3y) \end{bmatrix}$$

$$= 5x^2 + (2xy + 2xy) + 3y^2$$

$$= 5x^2 + 4xy + 3y^2$$

The equation

$$5x^2 + 4xy + 3y^2 = 5$$

can be written in matrix form

$$[x \quad y]\begin{bmatrix} 5 & 2 \\ 2 & 3 \end{bmatrix}\begin{bmatrix} x \\ y \end{bmatrix} = 5$$

The general homogeneous quadratic form $ax^2 + 2hxy + by^2 = 1$ can therefore be expressed in matrix form

$$[x \quad y]\begin{bmatrix} a & h \\ h & b \end{bmatrix}\begin{bmatrix} x \\ y \end{bmatrix} = 1$$

The equation $ax^2 + 2hxy + by^2 = 1$ represents a conic section and by choosing suitable values for the elements a, b, h of the matrix, the matrix form can be used to represent the circle, ellipse, hyperbola and so on. By a suitable transformation the axes of the conic can be rotated if this is necessary.

The general quadratic form

$$[x \quad y]\begin{bmatrix} a & h \\ h & b \end{bmatrix}\begin{bmatrix} x \\ y \end{bmatrix}$$

can be written more briefly $X^t A X$ since the row matrix is the transpose of the column matrix and $A = \begin{bmatrix} a & h \\ h & b \end{bmatrix}$.

If $A = \begin{bmatrix} a^2 & 0 \\ 0 & b^2 \end{bmatrix}$

the equation

$$[x \quad y]\begin{bmatrix} a^2 & 0 \\ 0 & b^2 \end{bmatrix}\begin{bmatrix} x \\ y \end{bmatrix} = a^2 b^2$$

110

becomes

$$a^2x^2 + b^2y^2 = a^2b^2$$

or

$$\frac{x^2}{b^2} + \frac{y^2}{a^2} = 1 \qquad \text{i.e. the ellipse.}$$

If the column matrix $\begin{bmatrix} x \\ y \end{bmatrix}$ is replaced by $\begin{bmatrix} x^1 \\ y^1 \end{bmatrix}$ the equation

$[x \quad y]\begin{bmatrix} a & h \\ h & b \end{bmatrix}\begin{bmatrix} x' \\ y' \end{bmatrix} = 1$ represents the equation of the tangent to
the conic on page 110 at the point (x', y') or

$$X^tAX' = 1 \qquad \text{where} \qquad X' = \begin{bmatrix} x' \\ y' \end{bmatrix}$$

(3×3) Matrices and Quadratic Forms

Another matrix form using a column matrix $\begin{bmatrix} x \\ y \\ 1 \end{bmatrix}$ and its transpose is

$$[x \quad y \quad 1]\begin{bmatrix} a & h & g \\ h & b & f \\ g & f & c \end{bmatrix}\begin{bmatrix} x \\ y \\ 1 \end{bmatrix} = 0$$

The (3×3) matrix is observed to be SYMMETRIC since the elements in corresponding places on either side of the leading diagonal are equal, i.e. its transpose is equal to itself ($A^t = A$).

Multiplication of the three matrices gives

$$[x \quad y \quad 1]\begin{bmatrix} ax & by & g \\ bx & by & f \\ gx & fy & c \end{bmatrix} = 0$$

$$\Rightarrow \quad ax^2 + by^2 + 2bxy + 2gx + 2fy + c = 0$$

which is the general equation of the second degree and represents a conic.

The special case

$$[x \quad y \quad 1] \begin{bmatrix} 1 & 0 & g \\ 0 & 1 & f \\ g & f & c \end{bmatrix} \begin{bmatrix} x \\ y \\ 1 \end{bmatrix} = 0$$

gives

$$[x \quad y \quad 1] \begin{bmatrix} x+g \\ y+f \\ gx+fy+c \end{bmatrix} = 0$$

$$\Rightarrow \quad x^2 + gx + y^2 + fy + gx + fy + c = 0$$

i.e.

$$x^2 + y^2 + 2gx + 2fy + c = 0$$

familiar to most as the general equation of the circle. The tangent to the circle at the point $(x'y')$ is

$$[x \quad y \quad 1] \begin{bmatrix} 1 & 0 & g \\ 0 & 1 & f \\ g & f & c \end{bmatrix} \begin{bmatrix} x' \\ y' \\ 1 \end{bmatrix} = 0$$

or

$$xx' + yy' + g(x+x') + f(y+y') + c = 0$$

If $X = \begin{bmatrix} x \\ y \\ z \end{bmatrix}$, then $X^t = [x \quad y \quad z]$ and $A = \begin{bmatrix} a & h & g \\ h & b & f \\ g & f & c \end{bmatrix}$ then

$X^t A X = 1$ gives an homogeneous equation of the second degree in x, y and z representing a quadratic surface.

$X^t A X = 1$ on multiplication gives

$$ax^2 + by^2 + cz^2 + 2fyz + 2gzx + 2hxy = 1$$

Examples XXIV

1 Find the quadratic form equivalent to the matrix product

$$[x \quad y] \begin{bmatrix} 4 & 3 \\ 3 & 2 \end{bmatrix} \begin{bmatrix} x \\ y \end{bmatrix}.$$

2 Find the quadratic form equivalent to the matrix product

$$[x \quad y]\begin{bmatrix} 1 & 2 \\ 2 & 1 \end{bmatrix}\begin{bmatrix} x \\ y \end{bmatrix}.$$

3 Express the quadratic form $x^2 + 2xy + y^2$ in matrix notation.

4 Express $2x^2 + 6xy + 6y^2$ in matrix notation.

5 Express $2x^2 + 3xy + 6y^2$ in matrix notation.

6 Express $x^2 + y^2$ in matrix notation.

7 Express $x^2 + y^2 = 25$ in matrix notation.

8 Find the quadratic form equivalent to the matrix product

$$[x \quad y]\begin{bmatrix} 2 & 0 \\ 0 & 5 \end{bmatrix}\begin{bmatrix} x \\ y \end{bmatrix}.$$

9 Solve the matrix equation $[x \quad 2]\begin{bmatrix} 2 & 0 \\ 7 & \frac{3}{4} \end{bmatrix}\begin{bmatrix} x \\ 2 \end{bmatrix} = 0.$

10 Find the quadratic form represented by

$$[x \quad y \quad 1]\begin{bmatrix} 1 & 0 & 3 \\ 0 & 1 & 2 \\ 3 & 2 & -3 \end{bmatrix}\begin{bmatrix} x \\ y \\ 1 \end{bmatrix} = 0.$$

11 Give the circle $x^2 + y^2 + 6x - 8y + 9 = 0$ in matrix form.

12 Give the equation of the tangent to the circle

$$x^2 + y^2 + 6x - 8y + 9 = 0$$

at the point (x', y') in matrix form.

13 If $A = \begin{bmatrix} 1 & 0 & 3 \\ 0 & 1 & 2 \\ 3 & 2 & -3 \end{bmatrix}$, $X = \begin{bmatrix} x \\ y \\ z \end{bmatrix}$ give the quadratic form of the

matrix equation $X'AX = 0.$

113

General Definition of a Matrix

Throughout all the work done on (2×2), (3×3) and rectangular matrices, the *position* of the element of a matrix is of the greatest importance. The position of the element is completely defined by its row and column position.

Definition

A rectangular array of numbers (called ELEMENTS) containing m rows and n columns is called a MATRIX.

The elements are enclosed in square brackets (used throughout this book) or in curved brackets (widely used in many modern books). Each element is given two suffixes, the *first* to denote the *row* and the *second* the *column. This convention is always followed.*

$$
\begin{bmatrix}
a_{11} & a_{12} & a_{13} & \cdots & a_{1n} \\
a_{21} & a_{22} & a_{23} & \cdots & a_{2n} \\
\cdot & \cdot & \cdot & \cdot & \cdot \\
\cdot & \cdot & \cdot & \cdot & \cdot \\
a_{m1} & a_{m2} & a_{m3} & \cdots & a_{mn}
\end{bmatrix}
\text{ or }
\begin{pmatrix}
a_{11} & a_{12} & a_{13} & \cdots & a_{1n} \\
a_{21} & a_{22} & a_{23} & \cdots & a_{2n} \\
a_{31} & \cdot & \cdot & \cdot & \cdot \\
\cdot & \cdot & \cdot & \cdot & \cdot \\
a_{m1} & a_{m2} & a_{m3} & \cdots & a_{mn}
\end{pmatrix}
$$

In the above arrays a_{23} means the element in the *second* row and in the *third* column; a_{mn} means the element in the mth row and the nth column. The general element is *usually* denoted by a_{rs} or a_{ij}.

Abbreviated Notation

The notation for a matrix can be abbreviated still further and for theoretical work the contraction makes for simplicity of expression. The matrix shown in the previous paragraph can be denoted by $\|a_{ij}\|$ or $[a_{ij}]$ or (a_{ij}) or A. For some purposes it is useful to speak of one of the terms of the matrix and here another notation is used. If $[A]$ or (A) is the matrix A; then $[A]_{ij}$ or $(A)_{ij}$ means the element in the ith row and jth column of the matrix A.

The sum of two $(m \times n)$ matrices A and B is obtained by adding corresponding elements as

$$A = \|a_{ij}\| \qquad B = \|b_{ij}\|$$
$$A + B = \|a_{ij}\| + \|b_{ij}\| = \|a_{ij} + b_{ij}\|$$

But since the sum $(a_{ij} + b_{ij})$ is a sum of *numbers* these numbers obey the usual *commutative and associative laws for numbers*, we can write

$$A + B = \|a_{ij} + b_{ij}\| = \|b_{ij} + a_{ij}\| = B + A$$

$$(A + B) + C = \|a_{ij} + b_{ij}\| + \|c_{ij}\| = \|(a_{ij} + b_{ij}) + c_{ij}\|$$

$$= \|a_{ij} + (b_{ij} + c_{ij})\|$$

$$= \|a_{ij}\| + \|b_{ij} + c_{ij}\|$$

$$= A + (B + C)$$

If k is a scalar then

$$kA + kB = \|ka_{ij}\| + \|kb_{ij}\| = \|ka_{ij} + kb_{ij}\|$$

$$= \|k(a_{ij} + b_{ij})\|$$

$$= k(A + B)$$

Multiplication of Matrices

$$C = A.B$$

First we remember that matrices A and B must be conformable, i.e. the *number of columns* of A must be equal to the *number of rows* of B.

With A and B both (2×2) matrices each element of C, their product, was composed of the addition of two products.

With A and B both (3×3) matrices the elements of C were the result of addition of three products.

If A is an $(m \times n)$ matrix and B is an $(n \times l)$ matrix they are conformable and C will be a $(m \times l)$ matrix and each element of C will be the sum of n products.

$$[AB]_{ij} = \sum_{k=1}^{k=n} a_{ik}.b_{kj}$$

or

$$c_{ij} = \sum_{k=1}^{k=n} a_{ik}.b_{kj} = a_{i1}b_{1j} + a_{i2}b_{2j} + a_{i3}b_{3j}\ldots \ldots a_{in}b_{nj}$$

Summary of the Laws of Matrix Algebra

The laws of addition and multiplication given on page 56 for (2×2) matrices can now be extended to all matrices which are conformable and remembering that, in general, multiplication of matrices is *not* commutative. Some additional relationships covering inverses and transposes must be given.

The following laws are restated for all conformable matrices.

(i) $A + B = B + A$ (Commutative Law for addition.)

(ii) $(A + B) + C = A + (B + C)$ (Associative Law for addition.)

(iii) $A + O = O + A = A$ (Null or Zeromatrix is the Identity element for addition.)

(iv) $(AB)C = A(BC)$ (Associative Law for multiplication.)

(v) $(A + B)C = AC + BC$ (Distributive Law for multiplication.)
and
$C(A + B) = CA + CB$

(*Note:* the *order* of multiplication must be adhered to since multiplication is not commutative.)

(vi) $A.I = IA = A$ (Unit matrix is the Identity element for multiplication.)

The inverse of matrix A is denoted by A^{-1} but the Transpose of A can be denoted A^t *or* by A' either notation being acceptable.

Since A^t or A' results from the interchange of rows and columns

$$(A^t)^t = A$$

and if the product AB exists then it was shown earlier that

$$(AB)^t = B^t A^t$$

hence if ABC exists then

$$(ABC)^t = (AB.C)^t$$

$$= C^t.(AB)^t$$

$$= C^t.B^t.A^t$$

It can be shown also that since $A.A^{-1} = I$

$$(A^{-1})^t = (A^t)^{-1}$$

and if the product AB exists and A and B are non-singular then

$$(AB)^{-1} = B^{-1}A^{-1}$$

Examples XXV

$$A = \begin{bmatrix} 2 & 3 \\ 4 & 7 \end{bmatrix} \qquad B = \begin{bmatrix} -2 & 2 \\ -3 & 2 \end{bmatrix} \qquad C = \begin{bmatrix} 2 & -1 \\ 3 & 4 \end{bmatrix}$$

1 Find A^t, B^t, $(AB)^t$, $B^t.A^t$.

2 Find C^t, $(ABC)^t$, $C^t.(AB)^t$, $C^t.B^t.A^t$.

3 Find AB, $(AB)^{-1}$, $B^{-1}A^{-1}$.

4 Find $(C^{-1})^t$, $(C^t)^{-1}$ and state your conclusion.

5 $P = \begin{bmatrix} 1 & 0 & 3 \\ 2 & 1 & 4 \\ 0 & 1 & 3 \end{bmatrix} \qquad Q = \begin{bmatrix} 3 & 2 & 1 \\ 4 & 2 & 2 \\ 1 & 3 & 0 \end{bmatrix}$

(a) Find P^t, Q^t, $(PQ)^t$, $Q^t.P^t$.

(b) Find P^{-1}, Q^{-1}, $(PQ)^{-1}$, $Q^{-1}P^{-1}$.

6 Since $A.A^{-1} = I$ and $I^t = I$, prove that $(A^{-1})^t = (A^t)^{-1}$.

7 Why is $(A-B)(A+B)$, in general, not the same as $A^2 - B^2$?

8 Expand $(I-A)(I+A)$.

Linear Dependence and Rank

The concepts of Rank and Linear Dependence are of the utmost importance in the further applications of matrix algebra.

Linearly Dependent Quantities

A set of "quantities" $x_1, x_2, x_3 \ldots x_n$ is said to be linearly dependent if there is a linear combination of them equal to zero,

$$a_1x_1 + a_2x_2 + a_3x_3 + \ldots a_nx_n = 0$$

with coefficients a_1, a_2, $a_3 \ldots a_n$ in the field of numbers in which one is working and not all these coefficients being zero.

If the only relation possible is given when $a_1 = a_2 = a_3 \ldots a_n = 0$ then the quantities are said to be *linearly independent*.

Example (i)

The quantities $x+2y$ and $3x+6y$ are linearly dependent because

$$-3(x+2y)+(3x+6y) \equiv 0$$

117

Introduction to Matrices

Example (ii)

The quantities $(-x+2y+3z)$, $(x-4y-13z)$ and $(-3x+5y+4z)$ are linearly dependent since

$$7(-x+2y+3z)+(x-4y-13z)-2(-3x+5y+4z) = 0$$

Example (iii)

The quantities $(-x+2y-3z)$, $(2x-y+4z)$ and $(3x+4y+z)$ are linearly independent because if

$$a(-x+2y-3z)+b(2x-y+4z)+c(3x+4y+z) = 0$$

this leads to the three relations

$$x(-a+2b+3c) = 0 \Rightarrow -a+2b+3c = 0$$

$$y(2a-b+4c) = 0 \Rightarrow 2a-b+4c = 0$$

$$z(-3a+4b+c) = 0 \Rightarrow -3a+4b+c = 0$$

Eliminating a gives

$$2b+8c = 0$$

and

$$3b+10c = 0$$

which is only possible if $b = 0$ and $c = 0$ and therefore $a = 0$.

Hence by definition $(-x+2y-3z)$, $(2x-y+4z)$, $(3x+4y+z)$ are linearly independent.

Example (iv)

The three vectors $\begin{bmatrix} 3 \\ 2 \\ 4 \end{bmatrix}$, $\begin{bmatrix} 2 \\ 0 \\ 2 \end{bmatrix}$, $\begin{bmatrix} 4 \\ 2 \\ 3 \end{bmatrix}$ are linearly independent because

the relation $a\begin{bmatrix} 3 \\ 2 \\ 4 \end{bmatrix} + b\begin{bmatrix} 2 \\ 0 \\ 2 \end{bmatrix} + c\begin{bmatrix} 4 \\ 2 \\ 3 \end{bmatrix} = \begin{bmatrix} 0 \\ 0 \\ 0 \end{bmatrix}$ leads to

$$\begin{bmatrix} 3a \\ 2a \\ 4a \end{bmatrix} + \begin{bmatrix} 2b \\ 0 \\ 2b \end{bmatrix} + \begin{bmatrix} 4c \\ 2c \\ 3c \end{bmatrix} = \begin{bmatrix} 0 \\ 0 \\ 0 \end{bmatrix}$$

$$\begin{bmatrix} 3a+2b+4c \\ 2a \quad +2c \\ 4a+2b+3c \end{bmatrix} = \begin{bmatrix} 0 \\ 0 \\ 0 \end{bmatrix}$$

for these two column matrices to be equal their corresponding elements must be equal

$$3a+2b+4c = 0$$
$$2a \quad +2c = 0$$
$$4a+2b+3c = 0$$

and the only possible solution is

$$a = b = c = 0$$

Examples XXVI

1 Show that $(x+2y)$ and $(3x-4y)$ are linearly independent.

2 Show that the quantities $(x+3y)$ and $(2x-6y)$ are linearly independent.

3 Are the vectors $\begin{bmatrix} 2 \\ 4 \end{bmatrix}$ and $\begin{bmatrix} 1 \\ 3 \end{bmatrix}$ linearly dependent?

4 Are the quantities $(2x-3y+4z)$, $(3x+4y-z)$ and $(-6x-5y-2z)$ linearly dependent?

5 What is the condition that $(ax+by)$ and $(cx+dy)$ are linearly dependent quantities?

6 If $p = (2x+y+z)$, $q = (3x-4y+6z)$ and $r = (4x-9y+11)$ find the relation between p, q, r for linear dependence. Calculate
$$\begin{vmatrix} 2 & 1 & 1 \\ 3 & -4 & 6 \\ 4 & -9 & 11 \end{vmatrix}$$
and state your conclusion.

7 If $n = (2x+y+z)$, $m = (x+2y+2z)$ and $p = (x+3y+2z)$ are the quantities n, m and p linearly dependent?

8 Are the vectors $\begin{bmatrix} 2 \\ 1 \\ 4 \end{bmatrix}$, $\begin{bmatrix} -1 \\ 2 \\ -7 \end{bmatrix}$, $\begin{bmatrix} 3 \\ 4 \\ 1 \end{bmatrix}$ linearly dependent?

9 Calculate the value of $\begin{vmatrix} 2 & -1 & 3 \\ 1 & 2 & 4 \\ 4 & -1 & 1 \end{vmatrix}$ and compare with the result

of question 8. State your conclusion.

Rank of a Matrix

Definition

The RANK of a matrix A is defined as the maximum number of linearly independent rows of A.

It can be shown that RANK defined in this way is also equal to the order of the largest non-zero (or non-vanishing) minor of the determinant of that matrix.

Matrix $A = \begin{bmatrix} 3 & 2 \\ 1 & 4 \end{bmatrix}$.

The rows (3 2) and (1 4) are linearly dependent if

$$a(3 \quad 2) + b(1 \quad 4) = 0$$

$$\Rightarrow 3a + b = 0 \qquad a = 0$$
$$\Rightarrow \qquad$$
$$\Rightarrow 2a + 4b = 0 \qquad b = 0$$

The rows are linearly independent, hence the rank is 2.

Matrix $B = \begin{bmatrix} 3 & 1 \\ 6 & 2 \end{bmatrix}$ and $a(3 \quad 1) + b(6 \quad 2) = 0$ is satisfied by

$a = 2, b = 1$.

The rows are linearly dependent and the rank is less than 2 but equal to 1 because there are non-zero elements in the minors. Only the null matrix has rank of zero.

Notice that $\det|A| = 10$ hence rank is 2 but $\det|B| = 0$ hence rank is less than 2, i.e. 1.

Consider the rows of the matrix $P = \begin{bmatrix} 3 & 4 & 1 \\ 4 & 3 & 2 \\ 2 & 1 & 4 \end{bmatrix}$

$$a(3 \quad 4 \quad 1) + b(4 \quad 3 \quad 2) + c(2 \quad 1 \quad 4) = 0$$

$$\Rightarrow 3a + 4b + 2c = 0$$

$$4a + 3b + c = 0$$

$$a + 2b + 4c = 0$$

From the first two equations $\qquad -5a - 2b = 0$
From the last two equations $\qquad -15a - 10b = 0$
and therefore the only possible solution is $a = b = c = 0$. The three rows are linearly independent, the rank is 3.

Had we used columns instead of rows for testing we would have found

$$a\begin{bmatrix} 3 \\ 4 \\ 2 \end{bmatrix} + b\begin{bmatrix} 4 \\ 3 \\ 1 \end{bmatrix} + c\begin{bmatrix} 1 \\ 2 \\ 4 \end{bmatrix} = \begin{bmatrix} 0 \\ 0 \\ 0 \end{bmatrix}$$

resulted in

$$3a + 4b + c = 0$$

$$4a + 3b + 2c = 0$$

$$2a + b + 4c = 0$$

and again the only solution is $a = b = c = 0$.

The determinant $\begin{vmatrix} 3 & 4 & 1 \\ 4 & 3 & 2 \\ 2 & 1 & 4 \end{vmatrix} = -20$ and it is from a (3×3) matrix.

Therefore it is of *order* 3, hence the rank is 3.

The matrix $Q = \begin{bmatrix} 3 & 5 & -15 \\ 4 & 3 & 2 \\ 2 & 1 & 4 \end{bmatrix}$ has its three rows linearly dependent because they can be expressed in the linear relationship

$$a(3 \quad 5 \quad -15) + b(4 \quad 3 \quad 2) + c(2 \quad 1 \quad 4) = 0$$

where $a = 1$, $b = -3\frac{1}{2}$ and $c = 5\frac{1}{2}$. The rank is less than 3 but since any two of the rows are linearly independent then the rank is 2.

Notice that the determinant of Q is 0 but any (2×2) sub-matrix has a non-zero determinant, the rank is 2.

E

The 3×4 rectangular matrix $R = \begin{bmatrix} 3 & 2 & 1 & 8 \\ 4 & 3 & 1 & 2 \\ 1 & 2 & 1 & 6 \end{bmatrix}$ has only 3 rows

but 4 columns.

The four column vectors are linearly dependent since if

$$a\begin{bmatrix} 3 \\ 4 \\ 1 \end{bmatrix} + b\begin{bmatrix} 2 \\ 3 \\ 2 \end{bmatrix} + c\begin{bmatrix} 1 \\ 1 \\ 1 \end{bmatrix} + d\begin{bmatrix} 8 \\ 2 \\ 6 \end{bmatrix} = 0$$

then $a = 1$, $b = -7$, $c = 19$ and $d = -1$ is a possible solution and therefore by definition the four columns are linearly dependent, however any three columns are linearly independent. The three row vectors [3 2 1 8], [4 3 1 2], [1 2 1 6] are, however, linearly independent. Hence the rank calculated by columns is 3 and the rank calculated from rows is 3. This illustrates an important property of any matrix that

$$\text{Row Rank} = \text{Column Rank}$$

The matrix

$$S = \begin{bmatrix} 1 & 2 & 1 & 3 \\ 2 & 0 & 4 & 1 \\ 1 & 6 & 8 & 2 \\ -1 & -2 & 4 & 1 \end{bmatrix}$$

is a square (4×4) matrix of order 4.

Hence its rank could be 4, 3, 2, or 1.

Calculation shows that the four row vectors are linearly independent, the rank is 4.

The diagonal matrix

$$D = \begin{bmatrix} a & 0 & 0 & 0 & 0 \\ 0 & b & 0 & 0 & 0 \\ 0 & 0 & c & 0 & 0 \\ 0 & 0 & 0 & d & 0 \\ 0 & 0 & 0 & 0 & e \end{bmatrix}$$

has one non-zero element in each row on the leading diagonal and inspection shows that the rank must be equal to the number of non-zero elements along the diagonal. Rank of any diagonal matrix can *be seen by inspection.*

It is a property of a matrix that the *Rank* remains *invariant* during any of the ELEMENTARY TRANSFORMATIONS previously defined. By reducing a large matrix using elementary transformations to an EQUIVALENT diagonal form, its rank can be seen by inspection and is equal to the number of non-zero elements on the leading diagonal.

Example

The method will be illustrated by using the (3×3) matrix
$M = \begin{bmatrix} 3 & 2 & 2 \\ 1 & 1 & 4 \\ 2 & 3 & 2 \end{bmatrix}$ and the transformations will be listed. The

sign $\sim$ means *equivalent* to.

$\begin{bmatrix} 3 & 2 & 2 \\ 1 & 1 & 4 \\ 2 & 3 & 2 \end{bmatrix}$ Divide row 1 by 3 and row 3 by 2.

$\sim \begin{bmatrix} 1 & \frac{2}{3} & \frac{2}{3} \\ 1 & 1 & 4 \\ 1 & \frac{3}{2} & 1 \end{bmatrix}$ Subtract row 1 from row 2 *and* row 3.

$\sim \begin{bmatrix} 1 & \frac{2}{3} & \frac{2}{3} \\ 0 & \frac{1}{3} & 3\frac{1}{3} \\ 0 & \frac{5}{6} & \frac{1}{3} \end{bmatrix}$ Subtract $2 \times$ row 2 from row 1 and 10×2 row 3 from row 2.

$\sim \begin{bmatrix} 1 & 0 & -6 \\ 0 & -8 & 0 \\ 0 & \frac{5}{6} & \frac{1}{3} \end{bmatrix}$ Add $\frac{5}{48} \times$ row 2 to row 3.

$\sim \begin{bmatrix} 1 & 0 & -6 \\ 0 & -8 & 0 \\ 0 & 0 & \frac{1}{3} \end{bmatrix}$ Add $18 \times$ row 3 to row 1.

$$\sim \begin{bmatrix} 1 & 0 & 0 \\ 0 & -8 & 0 \\ 0 & 0 & \frac{1}{3} \end{bmatrix}$$

This matrix is now in diagonal form, its rank is 3 and since the rank has remained invariant throughout, the rank of matrix M is 3.

Examples XXVII

1 What is the rank of $A = \begin{bmatrix} 2 & -1 \\ 3 & 4 \end{bmatrix}$?

2 What is the rank of $B = \begin{bmatrix} 3 & 2 & 4 \\ 2 & 0 & 2 \\ 4 & 2 & 3 \end{bmatrix}$?

3 What is the rank of $C = \begin{bmatrix} 2 & 3 \\ 3 & 5 \end{bmatrix}$?

4 What is the rank of $D = \begin{bmatrix} 2 & 4 \\ 2 & 4 \end{bmatrix}$ and find $|D|$?

5 What is the rank of $E = \begin{bmatrix} -1 & 2 & 3 \\ 1 & -4 & -13 \\ -3 & 5 & 5 \end{bmatrix}$ and find $|E|$.

6 Reduce $S = \begin{bmatrix} 1 & 2 & 1 & 3 \\ 2 & 0 & 4 & 1 \\ 1 & 6 & 8 & 2 \\ -1 & -2 & 4 & 1 \end{bmatrix}$ by elementary transformations

to an equivalent diagonal form and deduce the rank of S.

Rank and Consistency of Linear Equations

The concept of rank can be used to state the condition for consistency of a group of simultaneous linear equations. m linear equations in n unknowns are consistent when, and only when, the RANK of the matrix of the coefficients is equal to the rank of the *augmented matrix*. The Augmented Matrix is the matrix of coefficients to which the column of values (18 10 29 in the example below) has been inserted as a final column.

Example

$$4x + 3y + z = 18$$

$$2x + y + 3z = 10$$

$$5x + 7y - 2z = 29$$

The matrix of the coefficients is $\begin{bmatrix} 4 & 3 & 1 \\ 2 & 1 & 3 \\ 5 & 7 & -2 \end{bmatrix}$.

The rank of this matrix is 3.

The augmented matrix is $\begin{bmatrix} 4 & 3 & 1 & 18 \\ 2 & 1 & 3 & 10 \\ 5 & 7 & -2 & 29 \end{bmatrix}$ and the rank of this matrix is 3.

Since the rank of the augmented matrix is equal to the rank of the coefficient matrix the set of equations is consistent, i.e. these equations are satisfied by some set of values of x, y and z.

But if

$$4x + 3y + z = 0$$

$$2x + y + 3z = 0$$

$$5x + 7y - 2z = 0$$

the matrix of coefficients is again $\begin{bmatrix} 4 & 3 & 1 \\ 2 & 1 & 3 \\ 5 & 7 & -2 \end{bmatrix}$.

The above set of homogeneous equations can be expressed as $AX = 0$ where A is the matrix of coefficients and X is the column matrix $\begin{bmatrix} x \\ y \\ z \end{bmatrix}$.

Since $|A| \neq 0$ then $X = 0$, i.e. there is only the Trivial solution $x = 0$, $y = 0$, $z = 0$.

The application of matrix algebra to the study of Linear Equations is an important branch of Modern Algebra and is dealt with more fully in a number of the books in the bibliography (6, 7, 9, 10, 15).

Rank and Image Space

A line is one-dimensional, an area is two-dimensional, a volume is three-dimensional, a space of n dimensions is spanned by hyper-volume!

Three linearly independent vectors are needed to span three-dimensional space, and two linearly independent vectors to span two-dimensional space.

From this we can give some geometrical illustration of rank.

The (2×2) matrix represents a transformation and if the rank is 2 the image produced will be in two dimensions. If the rank is 1, then the image will be one-dimensional, i.e. a line not an area. This was shown on page 36 in diagram 16.

The (3×3) matrix represents a transformation in three dimensions—generally the unit cube transforms to a parallelepiped, if the rank of the matrix is 3. If the rank is 2, the image of the unit cube is in two dimensions only. (This follows because if the rank is only 2 the determinant of the matrix is zero hence the volume of the parallelepiped is zero also, i.e. it has become an area.)

Generally then the rank of a matrix is the dimension of the image space.

History of Matrices and Determinants

The form in which we use matrices is due largely to the work of Cayley, 1841, and Sylvester, 1839, in the early part of last century, but the use of determinants with a poorer form of symbolism had a much longer history mainly in connection with the solution of simultaneous equations.

Eight hundred years ago the Chinese were solving linear equations by using rods on a calculating board and developed the idea of elimination which was virtually a method of subtracting rows and columns of a determinant.

A Japanese mathematician, Seki Kowa, in a book written about 1683, showed some understanding of determinants which he used for elimination of unknowns from sets of linear simultaneous equations.

The theory of determinants was first developed in Europe by Leibnitz again in relation to the solution of simultaneous equations but the symbolism was unlike our own. Vandermonde in 1771 laid the foundations of modern theories of determinants as functions independent of any applications to linear equations.

Laplace (1772) showed how to expand a determinant in terms of its minors and Lagrange in 1773 treated determinants of the second and third orders. Gauss (1801) advanced the theory of the subject and in 1812 Binet showed how to multiply two matrices. About the same period Cauchy finally established the use of the word 'determinant' in its present sense and made great contributions to the advancement of the theoretical treatment of determinants. The work and contributions of the great mathematician, Jacobi (1839), in this field are remembered by naming certain forms of matrices after him. From this time (1839) forward the symbolism and theory of matrices received its greatest contributions from the work of Cayley (1821–1895) and Sylvester (1814–1897).

In 1850, Sylvester used the word MATRIX for arrays of numbers from which determinants could be formed and the theory of determinants is now regarded as a branch of matrix theory. During the early part of the nineteenth century determinant theory was applied intensively to the study of systems of linear equations, but the concepts of rank and linear dependence of a matrix which Sylvester developed, have produced a new outlook in the treatment of linear equations; the rapid development of the high speed computer from 1946 onwards and the wide applications of linear programming (1947) have hastened the change in approach.

In 1841 Cayley introduced the determinant notation which is now in general use and has been since he first announced it, then in 1858 he defined the square matrix in the form which has become standard and he continued to contribute important theory of the subject which the student will meet later.

Sir W. R. Hamilton discovered the principle of Quaternions in 1843 and published the full treatment in 1853 and it is in this connection that he is usually remembered but he made extensive and valuable contributions to matrix theory which he used in his own work.

Calculations with matrices were much simplified by the use of elementary transformations due to Grassman, 1862, and Kronecker, 1866, while Frobenius (1870–1911) developed ideas in equivalence in the theory of matrices.

So far in this *Introduction to Matrices*, the elements have been in the field of real numbers but elements in the complex number field can be used and the subject pushed deeper: complex matrices can be used in the representation of quaternions.

Bibliography

1 IRVING ADLER. *The New Mathematics.* Cygnet (paperback).

2 W. W. SAWYER. *Prelude to Mathematics.* Penguin.

3 G. MATTHEWS. *Matrices 1.* Edward Arnold.

4 G. MATTHEWS. *Matrices 2.* Edward Arnold.

5 A. MARY TROPPER. *Matrix Theory for Electrical Engineering Students.* Harrap.

6 M. M. NICHOLSON. *Fundamentals and Techniques of Mathematics for Scientists.* Longmans.

7 G. STEPHENSON. *Mathematical Methods for Science Students.* Longmans.

8 G. BIRKHOFF and S. MACLANE. *A Survey of Modern Algebra.* Macmillan.

9 W. L. FERRAR. *Algebra: A Textbook of Determinants, Matrices and Algebraic Forms.* Oxford University Press.

10 F. BOWMAN. *Matrices and Determinants.* E.U.P.

11 D. C. MURDOCH. *Linear Algebra for Undergraduates.* Wiley.

12 V. N. FADDEEVA. *Computational Methods of Linear Algebra,* trans. from Russian by Curtis D. Webster. Dover Pub. Inc.

13 A. C. AITKIN. *Determinants and Matrices.* Oliver and Boyd.

14 *Synopses for Modern Secondary School Mathematics.* O.E.E.C., Paris.

15 F. AYRES, JR. *Theory and Problems of Matrices.* Schaum Pub. Co., New York.

16 *Secret Codes: remainder arithmetic and matrices.* National Council of Teachers of Mathematics, Washington, U.S.A.

17 BRYAN THWAITES. *On Teaching Mathematics.* Pergamon.

18 *The Teaching of Algebra in Sixth Forms.* Mathematical Association Report, Bell.

Answers

Examples I

1 (i) $\begin{bmatrix} y_1 \\ y_2 \end{bmatrix} = \begin{bmatrix} 2 & 3 \\ 4 & 2 \end{bmatrix} \begin{bmatrix} x_1 \\ x_2 \end{bmatrix}$ (ii) $\begin{bmatrix} y_1 \\ y_2 \end{bmatrix} = \begin{bmatrix} 10 & 12 \\ 25 & 16 \end{bmatrix} \begin{bmatrix} x_1 \\ x_2 \end{bmatrix}$

(iii) $\begin{bmatrix} x' \\ y' \end{bmatrix} = \begin{bmatrix} 3 & 2 \\ 2 & 3 \end{bmatrix} \begin{bmatrix} x \\ y \end{bmatrix}$ (iv) $\begin{bmatrix} x' \\ y' \end{bmatrix} = \begin{bmatrix} 4 & -3 \\ 2 & -1 \end{bmatrix} \begin{bmatrix} x \\ y \end{bmatrix}$

2 (i) $x' = 2x + y$ (ii) $x' = 3x + y$

$\qquad y' = 4x + 6y$ $y' = 2y$

3 $C = \begin{bmatrix} 6 & 9 \\ 6 & 11 \end{bmatrix}$ $D = \begin{bmatrix} 2 & 3 \\ 4 & 3 \end{bmatrix}$

4 $B + A = \begin{bmatrix} 6 & 9 \\ 6 & 11 \end{bmatrix}$ $A + B = B + A$

5 $P + Q = \begin{bmatrix} 3 & 5 \\ 4 & 10 \end{bmatrix}$ $Q + R = \begin{bmatrix} 2 & 4 \\ 6 & 5 \end{bmatrix}$

$(P + Q) + R = \begin{bmatrix} 3 & 5 \\ 4 & 10 \end{bmatrix} + \begin{bmatrix} 1 & 2 \\ 3 & 1 \end{bmatrix} = \begin{bmatrix} 4 & 7 \\ 7 & 11 \end{bmatrix}$

$P + (Q + R) = \begin{bmatrix} 2 & 3 \\ 1 & 6 \end{bmatrix} + \begin{bmatrix} 2 & 4 \\ 6 & 5 \end{bmatrix} = \begin{bmatrix} 4 & 7 \\ 7 & 11 \end{bmatrix}$

6 $Q + P = \begin{bmatrix} 3 & 5 \\ 4 & 10 \end{bmatrix}$ $Q + P = P + Q$

$R + Q = \begin{bmatrix} 2 & 4 \\ 6 & 5 \end{bmatrix}$ $R + Q = Q + R$

7 $(P - Q) = \begin{bmatrix} 1 & 1 \\ -2 & 2 \end{bmatrix}$ $(Q - R) = \begin{bmatrix} 0 & 0 \\ 0 & 3 \end{bmatrix}$

$(P - Q) - R = \begin{bmatrix} 0 & -1 \\ -5 & 1 \end{bmatrix}$ $P - (Q - R) = \begin{bmatrix} 2 & 3 \\ 1 & 3 \end{bmatrix}$

$$(P-Q)+R = \begin{bmatrix} 2 & 3 \\ 1 & 3 \end{bmatrix}$$

Examples II

1 $A.B = \begin{bmatrix} 11 & 16 \\ 19 & 26 \end{bmatrix}$ $\qquad$ $B.A = \begin{bmatrix} 4 & 15 \\ 10 & 33 \end{bmatrix}$

2 $P.Q = \begin{bmatrix} 3 & -6 \\ -1 & 2 \end{bmatrix}$ $\qquad$ $Q.P = \begin{bmatrix} 5 & 0 \\ -10 & 0 \end{bmatrix}.$

3 $A.B = \begin{bmatrix} 11 & 16 \\ 19 & 26 \end{bmatrix}$ $\qquad$ $(A.B)P = \begin{bmatrix} 59 & 38 \\ 97 & 64 \end{bmatrix}$

$\quad$ $B.P = \begin{bmatrix} 7 & 4 \\ 15 & 10 \end{bmatrix}$ $\qquad$ $A.(B.P) = \begin{bmatrix} 59 & 38 \\ 97 & 64 \end{bmatrix}$

$\quad (AB)P = A(BP)$

4 $B.A = \begin{bmatrix} 4 & 15 \\ 10 & 33 \end{bmatrix}$ $\qquad$ $(BA)P = \begin{bmatrix} 49 & 23 \\ 109 & 53 \end{bmatrix}$

$\quad$ $A.P = \begin{bmatrix} 11 & 7 \\ 19 & 8 \end{bmatrix}$ $\qquad$ $B.(AP) = \begin{bmatrix} 49 & 23 \\ 109 & 53 \end{bmatrix}$

$\quad (BA)P = B(AP)$

5 $A+B = \begin{bmatrix} 3 & 5 \\ 4 & 10 \end{bmatrix}$ $\qquad$ $P(A+B) = \begin{bmatrix} 11 & 25 \\ 13 & 25 \end{bmatrix}$

$\quad$ $PA = \begin{bmatrix} 4 & 15 \\ 7 & 15 \end{bmatrix}$ $\qquad$ $PB = \begin{bmatrix} 7 & 10 \\ 6 & 10 \end{bmatrix}$

$\quad$ $PA+PB = \begin{bmatrix} 11 & 25 \\ 13 & 25 \end{bmatrix}$ $\qquad$ $P(A+B) = PA+PB$

$\quad$ $B+P = \begin{bmatrix} 2 & 4 \\ 6 & 5 \end{bmatrix}$ $\qquad$ $A(B+P) = \begin{bmatrix} 22 & 23 \\ 38 & 34 \end{bmatrix}$

$\quad$ $AB = \begin{bmatrix} 11 & 16 \\ 19 & 26 \end{bmatrix}$ $\qquad$ $AP = \begin{bmatrix} 11 & 7 \\ 19 & 8 \end{bmatrix}$

$$AB + AP = \begin{bmatrix} 22 & 23 \\ 38 & 34 \end{bmatrix}$$

$$A(B + P) = AB + AP$$

6 Matrices do not obey commutative laws of multiplication.

$$AB \neq BA \qquad\qquad (AB)P \neq (BA)P$$

Examples III

1 $2A = \begin{bmatrix} 4 & 6 \\ 2 & 12 \end{bmatrix}$ $\qquad 5A = \begin{bmatrix} 10 & 15 \\ 5 & 30 \end{bmatrix}$ $\qquad -3A = \begin{bmatrix} -6 & -9 \\ -3 & -18 \end{bmatrix}$

$kA = \begin{bmatrix} 2k & 3k \\ k & 6k \end{bmatrix}$

2 $4B = \begin{bmatrix} 4 & 8 \\ 12 & 16 \end{bmatrix}$ $\qquad kB = \begin{bmatrix} k & 2k \\ 3k & 4k \end{bmatrix}$ $\qquad -2B = \begin{bmatrix} -2 & -4 \\ -6 & -8 \end{bmatrix}$

3 $2P = \begin{bmatrix} 4 & -2 \\ 6 & -6 \end{bmatrix}$ $\qquad nP = \begin{bmatrix} 2n & -n \\ 3n & -3n \end{bmatrix}$ $\qquad -3P = \begin{bmatrix} -6 & 3 \\ -9 & 9 \end{bmatrix}$

4 $A + A = \begin{bmatrix} 4 & 6 \\ 2 & 12 \end{bmatrix} = 2A$

Examples IV

2 $DK = \begin{bmatrix} 6 & 8 \\ 2 & 12 \end{bmatrix} = KD$ $\qquad KE = \begin{bmatrix} 2a & 2b \\ 2c & 2d \end{bmatrix} = EK$

3 $MB = \begin{bmatrix} 2 & 0 \\ -1 & 0 \end{bmatrix}$ $\qquad BM = \begin{bmatrix} 2 & 0 \\ -1 & 0 \end{bmatrix}$

$IM = \begin{bmatrix} 2 & 0 \\ -1 & 0 \end{bmatrix}$ $\qquad IB = \begin{bmatrix} 1 & 0 \\ 1 & 3 \end{bmatrix}$

4 $A - I = \begin{bmatrix} 1 & 3 \\ 1 & 5 \end{bmatrix}$ $\qquad A - 3I = \begin{bmatrix} -1 & 3 \\ 1 & 3 \end{bmatrix}$

$2B - I = \begin{bmatrix} 1 & 4 \\ 6 & 7 \end{bmatrix}$ $\qquad B - kI = \begin{bmatrix} (1-k) & 2 \\ 3 & (4-k) \end{bmatrix}$

5 $\begin{bmatrix} 7 & 15 \\ 2 & 10 \end{bmatrix}$

Examples V

1 $\begin{bmatrix} 2 & 3 \\ 3 & 5 \end{bmatrix}$ $\qquad$ $\begin{bmatrix} x' \\ y' \end{bmatrix} = \begin{bmatrix} 2 & 3 \\ 3 & 5 \end{bmatrix}\begin{bmatrix} x \\ y \end{bmatrix}$

2 $\begin{bmatrix} x' \\ y' \end{bmatrix} = \begin{bmatrix} 3 & 0 \\ 0 & 1 \end{bmatrix}\begin{bmatrix} x \\ y \end{bmatrix}$ $\qquad$ This represents a shear.

3 $\begin{bmatrix} x' \\ y' \end{bmatrix} = \begin{bmatrix} -1 & 0 \\ 0 & 1 \end{bmatrix}\begin{bmatrix} x \\ y \end{bmatrix}$ $\qquad$ (2, 3) becomes $(-2, 3)$
$\qquad\qquad\qquad\qquad\qquad\qquad$ (3, 5) becomes $(-3, 5)$

5 The axes are rotated clockwise through $-60°$.

6

7 All lengths are doubled.

8 Both are shears, but the second is 3 times larger in the x axis than the first.

9

Examples VI

1 -2

2 32

3 0 $\qquad$ singular

4 $A^{-1} = \begin{bmatrix} 5 & -7 \\ -2 & 3 \end{bmatrix}$ $\qquad$ $AA^{-1} = A^{-1}A = I$

5 $\begin{bmatrix} -2 & 0 \\ 0 & -2 \end{bmatrix}$ $\qquad$ $\begin{bmatrix} 2 & 3 \\ 4 & 5 \end{bmatrix}^{-1} = -\frac{1}{2}\begin{bmatrix} 5 & -3 \\ -4 & 2 \end{bmatrix}$

6 $\begin{bmatrix} 11 & 4 \\ 1 & 8 \end{bmatrix}$ $\qquad$ $\begin{bmatrix} 67 & 41 \\ 29 & 19 \end{bmatrix}$ $\qquad$ $P^{-1} = \begin{bmatrix} 2 & -3 \\ -3 & 5 \end{bmatrix}$

7 $\begin{bmatrix} 20 & 4 \\ 10 & 22 \end{bmatrix}$ $\qquad$ TERM

8 $\dfrac{1}{13}\begin{bmatrix} 3 & -4 \\ -2 & 7 \end{bmatrix}$

9 $\dfrac{1}{(ps-qr)}\begin{bmatrix} s & -q \\ -r & p \end{bmatrix}$ $\qquad (ps-qr) \neq 0$

10 $-1\begin{bmatrix} 8 & 5 \\ -3 & -2 \end{bmatrix}$

11 $P'x' = 13, y' = 9$ $\qquad\qquad P''x'' = 2, y'' = 1$

$Q'x' = 33, y' = 23$ $\qquad\quad Q''x'' = 4, y'' = 3$

Conclusion: The images of P' and Q' due to the inverse matrix are the original points P and Q.

12 A non-singular matrix represents a REVERSIBLE MAPPING and the Inverse of the matrix reverses the mapping.

Examples VII

1 $\begin{bmatrix} x' \\ y' \end{bmatrix} = \begin{bmatrix} 4 & 5 \\ 2 & 3 \end{bmatrix}\begin{bmatrix} x \\ y \end{bmatrix}$

$0'$ is $(0, 0)$ $\qquad P'$ is $(4, 2)$ $\qquad Q'$ is $(9, 5)$ $\qquad R'$ is $(5, 3)$
The new area is 2 sq units.

$\triangle = \begin{vmatrix} 4 & 5 \\ 2 & 3 \end{vmatrix} = 2$ $\qquad\qquad$ New area $= \triangle \times$ Old area

2 Area $A'B'C'D' = 5$. Area $ABCD$ $\qquad \begin{vmatrix} 3 & 2 \\ 2 & 3 \end{vmatrix} = 5$

3 $\dfrac{A'B'C'}{ABC} = \dfrac{5}{1} = \begin{vmatrix} 3 & 2 \\ 2 & 3 \end{vmatrix}$

4 $\begin{vmatrix} 2 & 3 \\ 3 & 2 \end{vmatrix} = -\begin{vmatrix} 3 & 2 \\ 2 & 3 \end{vmatrix}$

Examples VIII

1 $\begin{bmatrix} 2 & 3 \\ 3 & 5 \end{bmatrix}\begin{bmatrix} x \\ y \end{bmatrix} = \begin{bmatrix} 18 \\ 29 \end{bmatrix}$

2 $2x - 3y = 4$
$2x + 3y = 6$

3 $P.X = \begin{bmatrix} 2x + 3y \\ 3x + 5y \end{bmatrix}$ $P^{-1}(PX) = \begin{bmatrix} x \\ y \end{bmatrix}$

4 $x = 3$ $y = 4$

5 $x = \frac{5}{2}$ $y = \frac{1}{3}$

6 $x = \frac{45}{7} = 6\frac{3}{7}$ $y = \frac{50}{7} = 7\frac{1}{7}$

7 $C = \begin{bmatrix} 11 & 1 \\ 15 & 2 \end{bmatrix}$

$z_1 = 2y_1 + 3y_2$ $y_1 = x_1 + 2x_2$ $z_1 = 11x_1 + x_2$
$z_2 = 3y_1 + 4y_2$ $y_2 = 3x_1 - x_2$ $z_2 = 15x_1 + 2x_2$

Examples IX

1 $P^t = \begin{bmatrix} 2 & -2 \\ 5 & 4 \end{bmatrix}$

2 $P' = \begin{bmatrix} 2 & 3 \\ 3 & 5 \end{bmatrix}$

3 $Q^{-1} = \begin{bmatrix} \cos \alpha & -\sin \alpha \\ \sin \alpha & \cos \alpha \end{bmatrix}$ $Q^t = \begin{bmatrix} \cos \alpha & -\sin \alpha \\ \sin \alpha & \cos \alpha \end{bmatrix}$

4 $R^{-1} = \begin{bmatrix} \cos x & \sin x \\ -\sin x & \cos x \end{bmatrix}$ $R^t = \begin{bmatrix} \cos x & \sin x \\ -\sin x & \cos x \end{bmatrix}$

5 Q and R are orthogonal.

6 $A' = \begin{bmatrix} 3 & 2 \\ 4 & 5 \end{bmatrix}$ $B' = \begin{bmatrix} 2 & 4 \\ 3 & 7 \end{bmatrix}$ $(AB)' = \begin{bmatrix} 22 & 24 \\ 37 & 41 \end{bmatrix}$

$A'B' = \begin{bmatrix} 12 & 26 \\ 23 & 51 \end{bmatrix}$ $B'A' = \begin{bmatrix} 22 & 24 \\ 37 & 41 \end{bmatrix}$

conclusion $(AB)' = B'A'$

7 $A = 7$ $A' = 7$
$B = 2$ $B' = 2$

8 $A' - B' = \begin{bmatrix} 5 & 6 \\ 7 & 12 \end{bmatrix}$ $\qquad (A - B)' = \begin{bmatrix} 5 & 6 \\ 7 & 12 \end{bmatrix}$

Examples X

1 $2 + 3i = \begin{bmatrix} 2 & 3 \\ -3 & 2 \end{bmatrix}$ $\qquad 3 + 2i = \begin{bmatrix} -3 & 2 \\ -2 & 3 \end{bmatrix}$

$(2 + 3i) + (3 + 2i) = \begin{bmatrix} 5 & 5 \\ -5 & 5 \end{bmatrix} = 5 + 5i$

2 $\begin{bmatrix} 4 & 1 \\ -1 & 4 \end{bmatrix} = 4 + i$

3 $(2 - 3i)(4 - 5i) = \begin{bmatrix} -7 & -22 \\ 22 & -7 \end{bmatrix} = -7 - 22i$

4 $\begin{bmatrix} -5 & 12 \\ -12 & -5 \end{bmatrix} = -5 + 12i$

5 $\dfrac{1}{13} \begin{bmatrix} 0 & 13 \\ -13 & 0 \end{bmatrix} = i$

6 $r \begin{bmatrix} \cos \theta & \sin \theta \\ -\sin \theta & \cos \theta \end{bmatrix}$

7 $z_1 = r_1 \begin{bmatrix} \cos \theta_1 & \sin \theta_1 \\ -\sin \theta_1 & \cos \theta_1 \end{bmatrix}; \quad z_2 = r_2 \begin{bmatrix} \cos \theta_2 & \sin \theta_2 \\ -\sin \theta_2 & \cos \theta_2 \end{bmatrix}$

$z_1 z_2 = r_1 r_2 \begin{bmatrix} \cos(\theta_1 + \theta_2) & \sin(\theta_1 + \theta_2) \\ -\sin(\theta_1 + \theta_2) & \cos(\theta_1 + \theta_2) \end{bmatrix}$

Examples XI

3 $\vec{OC} = \begin{bmatrix} 4 \\ 3 \end{bmatrix}$

4 $OPRQ$ is a *Parallelogram*

5 $ORAQ$ is a *Parallelogram*

Examples XII

1 $AH = \begin{bmatrix} 4 & 3 \\ 1 & -2 \end{bmatrix}$ $\qquad HA = \begin{bmatrix} -2 & 1 \\ 3 & 4 \end{bmatrix}$

2 $KB = \begin{bmatrix} 10 & -3 \\ 2 & -2 \end{bmatrix}$ $\qquad BK = \begin{bmatrix} 4 & 15 \\ 2 & 4 \end{bmatrix}$

3 $LC = \begin{bmatrix} 5 & -2 \\ -9 & 7 \end{bmatrix}$ $\qquad CL = \begin{bmatrix} 9 & -2 \\ -5 & 3 \end{bmatrix}$

4 $DN = \begin{bmatrix} 10 & 6 \\ 3 & -18 \end{bmatrix}$ $\qquad ND = \begin{bmatrix} 10 & 2 \\ 9 & -18 \end{bmatrix}$

5 $T^2 = \begin{bmatrix} 0 & 0 \\ 0 & 0 \end{bmatrix}$ $\quad TA = \begin{bmatrix} 0 & 9 \\ 0 & -6 \end{bmatrix}$ $\quad AT = \begin{bmatrix} 0 & 9 \\ 0 & -6 \end{bmatrix}$

6 $F^2 = \begin{bmatrix} 0 & 4 \\ 0 & 4 \end{bmatrix}$ $\quad FB = \begin{bmatrix} 4 & -4 \\ 4 & -4 \end{bmatrix}$ $\quad BF = \begin{bmatrix} 0 & 14 \\ 0 & 0 \end{bmatrix}$

7 $AP = \begin{bmatrix} -2a & -2b \\ -2c & -2d \end{bmatrix}$ $\; PA = \begin{bmatrix} -2a & -2b \\ -2c & -2d \end{bmatrix}$ $\; AB = \begin{bmatrix} 0 & -6 \\ -6 & 0 \end{bmatrix}$

$\quad BA = \begin{bmatrix} 0 & -6 \\ -6 & 0 \end{bmatrix}$ $\quad BP = \begin{bmatrix} 3c & 3d \\ 3a & 3b \end{bmatrix}$ $\quad PB = \begin{bmatrix} 3b & 3a \\ 3d & 3c \end{bmatrix}$

Examples XIII

1 $\begin{bmatrix} y_1 \\ y_2 \\ y_3 \end{bmatrix} = \begin{bmatrix} 2 & 3 & 4 \\ 1 & -2 & 3 \\ 3 & 2 & -2 \end{bmatrix} \begin{bmatrix} x_1 \\ x_2 \\ x_3 \end{bmatrix}$

2 $y_1 = 3x_1 + 2x_2 + x_3$

$\quad y_2 = -2x_1 + 3x_2 + 6x_3$

$\quad y_3 = x_1 - 2x_2 + x_3$

3 $P+Q = \begin{bmatrix} 4 & 4 & 2 \\ 7 & 4 & 3 \\ 3 & 6 & 3 \end{bmatrix}$ $\qquad Q+P = \begin{bmatrix} 4 & 4 & 2 \\ 7 & 4 & 3 \\ 3 & 6 & 3 \end{bmatrix}$

$Q-P = \begin{bmatrix} 2 & 0 & 0 \\ 1 & 0 & 1 \\ -1 & 0 & -1 \end{bmatrix}$

4 $3B = \begin{bmatrix} 3 & 6 & 3 \\ 9 & 6 & 9 \\ 6 & 3 & 6 \end{bmatrix}$ $\qquad kB = \begin{bmatrix} k & 2k & k \\ 3k & 2k & 3k \\ 2k & k & 2k \end{bmatrix}$

5 $P+Q = \begin{bmatrix} 2 & 3 & 2 \\ 3 & 1 & 3 \\ 6 & 3 & 5 \end{bmatrix}$ $\qquad (P+Q)+R = \begin{bmatrix} 3 & 3 & 3 \\ 5 & 2 & 6 \\ 7 & 5 & 8 \end{bmatrix}$

$Q+R = \begin{bmatrix} 2 & 1 & 2 \\ 4 & 2 & 5 \\ 4 & 4 & 6 \end{bmatrix}$ $\qquad P+(Q+R) = \begin{bmatrix} 3 & 3 & 3 \\ 5 & 2 & 6 \\ 7 & 5 & 8 \end{bmatrix}$

i.e. $(P+Q)+R = P+(Q+R)$, this verifies the Associative Law of Matrix Addition.

Examples XIV

1 $P.Q = \begin{bmatrix} 12 & 9 & 6 \\ 18 & 13 & 8 \\ 20 & 16 & 10 \end{bmatrix}$ $\qquad Q.P = \begin{bmatrix} 11 & 13 & 7 \\ 14 & 18 & 10 \\ 12 & 11 & 6 \end{bmatrix}$

2 $B.I = \begin{bmatrix} 1 & 1 & 2 \\ 2 & 3 & 2 \\ 1 & 2 & 1 \end{bmatrix} = B$ $\qquad kI = \begin{bmatrix} k & 0 & 0 \\ 0 & k & 0 \\ 0 & 0 & k \end{bmatrix}$

$B+kI = \begin{bmatrix} (1+k) & 1 & 2 \\ 2 & (3+k) & 2 \\ 1 & 2 & (1+k) \end{bmatrix}$

$$B - kI = \begin{bmatrix} (1-k) & 1 & 2 \\ 2 & (3-k) & 2 \\ 1 & 2 & (1-k) \end{bmatrix}$$

3 $P.Q = \begin{bmatrix} 8 & 4 & 0 \\ 4 & 2 & 4 \\ 11 & 5 & 7 \end{bmatrix}$ $\qquad (PQ)R = \begin{bmatrix} 16 & 4 & 4 \\ 12 & 10 & 14 \\ 28 & 19 & 25 \end{bmatrix}$

$Q.R = \begin{bmatrix} 2 & 2 & 2 \\ 2 & -3 & -5 \\ 10 & 8 & 12 \end{bmatrix}$ $\qquad P(QR) = \begin{bmatrix} 16 & 4 & 4 \\ 12 & 10 & 14 \\ 28 & 19 & 25 \end{bmatrix}$

$P(RQ) = \begin{bmatrix} 38 & 20 & 22 \\ 12 & 6 & 4 \\ 35 & 17 & 15 \end{bmatrix}$ $\qquad R(PQ) = \begin{bmatrix} -3 & -1 & -7 \\ 53 & 25 & 25 \\ 49 & 23 & 29 \end{bmatrix}$

4 $A.S = \begin{bmatrix} 6 & 6 & 4 \\ -4 & 9 & 24 \\ 2 & -6 & 16 \end{bmatrix}$ $\qquad A.T = \begin{bmatrix} 6 & -6 & 4 \\ -4 & -9 & -24 \\ 2 & 6 & -16 \end{bmatrix}$

$S.A = \begin{bmatrix} 6 & 4 & 2 \\ -6 & 9 & 18 \\ 4 & -8 & 16 \end{bmatrix}$ $\qquad T.A = \begin{bmatrix} 6 & 4 & 2 \\ 6 & -9 & -18 \\ -4 & 8 & -16 \end{bmatrix}$

$S^2 = \begin{bmatrix} 4 & 0 & 0 \\ 0 & 9 & 0 \\ 0 & 0 & 16 \end{bmatrix}$ $\qquad S.T = \begin{bmatrix} 4 & 0 & 0 \\ 0 & -9 & 0 \\ 0 & 0 & -16 \end{bmatrix}$

5 $A.V = \begin{bmatrix} 1 & 2 & 3 \\ 6 & 3 & -2 \\ 4 & -2 & 1 \end{bmatrix}$ $\qquad V.A = \begin{bmatrix} 1 & -2 & 4 \\ -2 & 3 & 6 \\ 3 & 2 & 1 \end{bmatrix}$

Examples XV

1 $|P| = -2$

2 $|Q| = -6$

3 $|A| = 5$

4 Singular

5 $C = A.B = \begin{bmatrix} 8 & 13 & 13 \\ 13 & 20 & 20 \\ 7 & 14 & 14 \end{bmatrix}$ C is singular

6 8

7 24

8 $|D| = 4$ $|E| = 4$

Examples XVI

1 $A^t = \begin{bmatrix} 1 & 3 & 2 \\ 2 & 2 & 3 \\ 3 & 1 & 2 \end{bmatrix}$

2 $B^t = \begin{bmatrix} 3 & -2 & 1 \\ 2 & 3 & -2 \\ 1 & 6 & 4 \end{bmatrix}$

4 $C = \begin{bmatrix} -4 & -2 & 10 \\ 1 & 2 & -7 \\ 2 & -2 & -2 \end{bmatrix}$

$[\text{ADJOINT } Q] = \begin{bmatrix} -4 & 1 & 2 \\ -2 & 2 & -2 \\ 10 & -7 & -2 \end{bmatrix} |Q| = -6$

$Q^{-1} = -\dfrac{1}{6} \begin{bmatrix} -4 & 1 & 2 \\ -2 & 2 & -2 \\ 10 & -7 & -2 \end{bmatrix}$

5 $A^{-1} = \dfrac{1}{5} \begin{bmatrix} -1 & 3 & -3 \\ -6 & 3 & 2 \\ 2 & -1 & 1 \end{bmatrix}$

6 $P^{-1} = -\dfrac{1}{2}\begin{bmatrix} 1 & -1 & 0 \\ -4 & 0 & 2 \\ 5 & 1 & -4 \end{bmatrix}$

7 $R^{-1} = -\dfrac{1}{8}\begin{bmatrix} -4 & 8 & 4 \\ -6 & 4 & 2 \\ -3 & 6 & 5 \end{bmatrix}$

8 $A^t = \begin{bmatrix} a & h & g \\ h & b & f \\ g & f & c \end{bmatrix}$

9 $PQ = \begin{bmatrix} 8 & 5 & 8 \\ 4 & 3 & 4 \\ 11 & 8 & 11 \end{bmatrix} \qquad P' = \begin{bmatrix} 1 & 1 & 3 \\ 2 & 0 & 1 \\ 1 & 1 & 2 \end{bmatrix}$

$Q' = \begin{bmatrix} 1 & 2 & 3 \\ 1 & 1 & 2 \\ 1 & 2 & 3 \end{bmatrix} \qquad Q.P = \begin{bmatrix} 5 & 3 & 4 \\ 8 & 6 & 7 \\ 14 & 9 & 11 \end{bmatrix}$

$P'Q' = \begin{bmatrix} 5 & 9 & 14 \\ 3 & 6 & 9 \\ 4 & 7 & 11 \end{bmatrix} \qquad Q'P' = \begin{bmatrix} 8 & 4 & 11 \\ 5 & 3 & 8 \\ 8 & 4 & 11 \end{bmatrix}$

$(P.Q)' = \begin{bmatrix} 8 & 4 & 11 \\ 5 & 3 & 8 \\ 8 & 4 & 11 \end{bmatrix} \qquad (QP)' = \begin{bmatrix} 5 & 9 & 14 \\ 3 & 6 & 9 \\ 4 & 7 & 11 \end{bmatrix}$

$(PQ)' = Q'P' \qquad \text{and} \qquad (QP)' = P'Q'$

10 $PQR = \begin{bmatrix} 26 & 21 & 47 \\ 14 & 11 & 25 \\ 38 & 30 & 68 \end{bmatrix} \qquad QR = \begin{bmatrix} 4 & 3 & 7 \\ 6 & 5 & 11 \\ 10 & 8 & 18 \end{bmatrix}$

$$P' = \begin{bmatrix} 1 & 1 & 3 \\ 2 & 0 & 1 \\ 1 & 1 & 2 \end{bmatrix} \qquad (QR)'P' = \begin{bmatrix} 26 & 14 & 38 \\ 21 & 11 & 30 \\ 47 & 25 & 68 \end{bmatrix}$$

$$R'Q' = \begin{bmatrix} 4 & 6 & 10 \\ 3 & 5 & 8 \\ 7 & 11 & 18 \end{bmatrix} \qquad R'Q'P' = \begin{bmatrix} 26 & 14 & 38 \\ 21 & 11 & 30 \\ 47 & 25 & 68 \end{bmatrix}$$

$$(PQR)' = \begin{bmatrix} 26 & 14 & 38 \\ 21 & 11 & 30 \\ 47 & 25 & 68 \end{bmatrix}$$

$$(PQR)' = (QR)'P' = R'Q'P'$$

Examples XVII

1 $\begin{bmatrix} 1 & 2 & 1 \\ 3 & 2 & 1 \\ 2 & 3 & 2 \end{bmatrix} \begin{bmatrix} x \\ y \\ z \end{bmatrix} = \begin{bmatrix} 0 \\ 2 \\ 2 \end{bmatrix}$

$$P^{-1} = -\frac{1}{2} \begin{bmatrix} 1 & -1 & 0 \\ -4 & 0 & 2 \\ 5 & 1 & -4 \end{bmatrix} \qquad \begin{bmatrix} x \\ y \\ z \end{bmatrix} = \begin{bmatrix} 1 \\ -2 \\ 3 \end{bmatrix}$$

$x = 1 \qquad y = -2 \qquad z = 3$

2 $\begin{bmatrix} -1 & 2 & 0 \\ -3 & 1 & 2 \\ 3 & 0 & -4 \end{bmatrix} \begin{bmatrix} x \\ y \\ z \end{bmatrix} = \begin{bmatrix} 5 \\ -1 \\ 9 \end{bmatrix}$

$\begin{bmatrix} x \\ y \\ z \end{bmatrix} = \begin{bmatrix} -1 \\ 2 \\ -3 \end{bmatrix}$ i.e. $x = -1 \qquad y = 2 \qquad z = -3$

3 $\begin{bmatrix} x \\ y \\ z \end{bmatrix} = \begin{bmatrix} 2 \\ 3 \\ 4 \end{bmatrix}$ i.e. $x = 2 \qquad y = 3 \qquad z = 4$

4 $\begin{bmatrix} x \\ y \\ z \end{bmatrix} = \begin{bmatrix} 1 \\ 3 \\ 2 \end{bmatrix}$ i.e. $x = 1$ $y = 3$ $z = 2$

Examples XVIII

1 $\begin{vmatrix} 1 & 0 & 3 \\ 2 & 1 & 4 \\ 0 & 1 & 3 \end{vmatrix} = 5$ $\qquad$ $\begin{vmatrix} 1 & 0 & 2 \\ 3 & 4 & 5 \\ 5 & 6 & 7 \end{vmatrix} = -6$

$\begin{vmatrix} 3 & 0 & 0 \\ 0 & 4 & 0 \\ 0 & 0 & 2 \end{vmatrix} = 24$

2 $|A| = 4$ $\qquad\qquad$ $|B| = -31$

3 M is singular

4 MN is singular

6 $|T| = 1$ $\qquad\qquad$ $|U| = 1$

7 $|A| = |TU| = |T|.|U| = 1$

Examples XIX

1 $A.D = \begin{bmatrix} 6 & -3 & -4 \\ 2 & 3 & 0 \\ 4 & -6 & 0 \end{bmatrix}$ $\quad$ $D.A = \begin{bmatrix} 6 & -2 & 4 \\ 3 & 3 & 0 \\ -4 & 4 & 0 \end{bmatrix}$

2 $B.D = \begin{bmatrix} 1 & 8 & 21 \\ 2 & 0 & 28 \\ 1 & 8 & 42 \end{bmatrix}$ $\quad$ $D.B = \begin{bmatrix} 1 & 2 & 3 \\ 8 & 0 & 16 \\ 7 & 14 & 42 \end{bmatrix}$

3 $|E| = -3$ $\quad$ $|F| = -6$ $\quad$ $|EF| = 18$

4 $|G| = -12$ $\quad$ $|G^2| = 144$ $\quad$ $|3G| = -324$

5 $BT = \begin{bmatrix} 3 & 2 & 2 \\ 1 & 2 & 2 \\ 3 & 1 & 0 \end{bmatrix}$ $\quad$ $TB = \begin{bmatrix} 4 & 0 & 4 \\ 1 & 1 & 2 \\ 3 & -2 & 0 \end{bmatrix}$

$$|B| = -4 \qquad |T| = 1 \qquad |BT| = |TB| = -4$$

6 $\quad TV = \begin{bmatrix} 2 & 1 & 0 \\ 1 & 1 & 0 \\ 0 & 0 & 1 \end{bmatrix} \qquad VT = \begin{bmatrix} 1 & 1 & 0 \\ 1 & 2 & 0 \\ 0 & 0 & 1 \end{bmatrix}$

$\qquad V^2 = \begin{bmatrix} 1 & 0 & 0 \\ 2 & 1 & 0 \\ 0 & 0 & 1 \end{bmatrix} \qquad T^2 = \begin{bmatrix} 1 & 2 & 0 \\ 0 & 1 & 0 \\ 0 & 0 & 1 \end{bmatrix}$

7 $\quad A = LU$

$= \begin{bmatrix} 1 & d & e \\ a & (ad+1) & (ae+f) \\ b & (bd+c) & (be+cf+1) \end{bmatrix}$

L and U are triangular matrices.

8 $\quad A = \begin{bmatrix} 1 & 0 & 0 \\ 2 & 1 & 0 \\ 3 & 1 & 1 \end{bmatrix}\begin{bmatrix} 1 & 2 & 2 \\ 0 & 1 & 4 \\ 0 & 0 & 1 \end{bmatrix}$

9 $\quad L^{-1} = \begin{bmatrix} 1 & 0 & 0 \\ -2 & 1 & 0 \\ -1 & -1 & 1 \end{bmatrix}$

10 $\quad |L| = 1$

$\qquad |U| = 1$

Examples XX

1 $\begin{bmatrix} 3 & -4 \\ -2 & 3 \end{bmatrix}\begin{bmatrix} 3 & 4 \\ 2 & 3 \end{bmatrix}\begin{bmatrix} 3 & -4 \\ -2 & 3 \end{bmatrix} = I = \begin{bmatrix} 3 & -4 \\ -2 & 3 \end{bmatrix}\begin{bmatrix} 3 & 4 \\ 2 & 3 \end{bmatrix}$

2 $\begin{vmatrix} -2 & 3 \\ 4 & -7 \end{vmatrix} = 2 \qquad \text{Inverse} = \frac{1}{2}\begin{bmatrix} -7 & -3 \\ -4 & -2 \end{bmatrix} = \begin{bmatrix} \frac{7}{2} & -\frac{3}{2} \\ -2 & -1 \end{bmatrix}$

3 $\begin{bmatrix} \frac{2}{3} & -\frac{1}{3} & 0 \\ 0 & -1 & 1 \\ -\frac{1}{3} & \frac{5}{3} & -1 \end{bmatrix}$ or $\frac{1}{3}\begin{bmatrix} 2 & -1 & 0 \\ 0 & -3 & 3 \\ -1 & 5 & -3 \end{bmatrix}$

4 $\frac{1}{5}\begin{bmatrix} -1 & 3 & -3 \\ -6 & 3 & 2 \\ 2 & -1 & 1 \end{bmatrix}$

5 $-\frac{1}{4}\begin{bmatrix} -6 & 3 & 2 \\ 2 & -1 & -2 \\ 10 & -7 & -2 \end{bmatrix}$

6 $-1\begin{bmatrix} 0 & 0 & -1 \\ 0 & -1 & 0 \\ -1 & 0 & 0 \end{bmatrix}$ or $\begin{bmatrix} 0 & 0 & 1 \\ 0 & 1 & 0 \\ 1 & 0 & 0 \end{bmatrix}$

Examples XXI

1 $|A - \lambda I| = 0$ $\lambda = 3$ or 1

2 $|B - \lambda I| = 0$ $\lambda = 4$ or 3

3 $\lambda = 1$ or -1

4 Eigenvectors $\begin{bmatrix} 3 \\ -4 \end{bmatrix}$ and $\begin{bmatrix} 2 \\ -3 \end{bmatrix}$

5 $Q = \begin{bmatrix} 3 & 2 \\ -4 & -3 \end{bmatrix}$ $Q^{-1} = -1\begin{bmatrix} -3 & -2 \\ 4 & 3 \end{bmatrix}$

     $M = \begin{bmatrix} 1 & 0 \\ 0 & 3 \end{bmatrix}$

6 $\lambda = 4$ or 3

     $Q = \begin{bmatrix} 1 & 1 \\ -1 & 0 \end{bmatrix}$ $Q^{-1} = \begin{bmatrix} 0 & -1 \\ 1 & 1 \end{bmatrix}$

     $M = Q^{-1}BQ$

$$= \begin{bmatrix} 4 & 0 \\ 0 & 3 \end{bmatrix}$$

7 Since $M = Q^{-1}BQ$, then M and B are similar matrices.

Examples XXII

1 Latent roots are $1, -1, 2$

2 Eigenvectors are $\begin{bmatrix} 1 \\ -1 \\ 0 \end{bmatrix} \begin{bmatrix} 1 \\ 0 \\ -1 \end{bmatrix} \begin{bmatrix} 1 \\ -1 \\ -1 \end{bmatrix}$

$$Q = \begin{bmatrix} 1 & 1 & 1 \\ -1 & 0 & -1 \\ 0 & -1 & -1 \end{bmatrix} \qquad Q^{-1} = \begin{bmatrix} 1 & 0 & 1 \\ 1 & 1 & 0 \\ -1 & -1 & -1 \end{bmatrix}$$

$$M = Q^{-1}AQ = \begin{bmatrix} 1 & 0 & 0 \\ 0 & -1 & 0 \\ 0 & 0 & 2 \end{bmatrix}$$

3 Latent roots are $2, 3, 4$

4 Eigenvectors are $\begin{bmatrix} 1 \\ -1 \\ 0 \end{bmatrix} \begin{bmatrix} 1 \\ 0 \\ -1 \end{bmatrix} \begin{bmatrix} 1 \\ -1 \\ -1 \end{bmatrix}$

$$Q = \begin{bmatrix} 1 & 1 & 1 \\ -1 & 0 & -1 \\ 0 & -1 & -1 \end{bmatrix} \qquad Q^{-1} = \begin{bmatrix} 1 & 0 & 1 \\ 1 & 1 & 0 \\ -1 & -1 & -1 \end{bmatrix}$$

$$M = Q^{-1}AQ = \begin{bmatrix} 2 & 0 & 0 \\ 0 & 3 & 0 \\ 0 & 0 & 4 \end{bmatrix}$$

Examples XXIII

1 $A(2 \times 4)$ $B(2 \times 2)$ $C(2 \times 4)$ $D(4 \times 2)$ $E(4 \times 4)$
    $F(4 \times 3)$ $G(3 \times 3)$

2 $A + C = \begin{bmatrix} 6 & 3 & 1 & 3 \\ 2 & 10 & 9 & 9 \end{bmatrix}$

3 $A.F\ (2 \times 4).(4 \times 3) = \begin{bmatrix} 19 & 5 & 26 \\ 34 & 10 & 84 \end{bmatrix}$ (2×3)

    $B.C\ (2 \times 2)(2 \times 4) = \begin{bmatrix} 21 & 18 & 21 & 30 \\ 7 & 6 & 7 & 10 \end{bmatrix}$

    $A.D\ (2 \times 4)(4 \times 2) = \begin{bmatrix} 28 & 5 \\ 67 & 63 \end{bmatrix}$ (2×2)

    $E.F\ (4 \times 4)(4 \times 3) = \begin{bmatrix} 19 & 5 & 28 \\ 38 & 10 & 62 \\ 4 & -1 & 10 \\ 27 & 8 & 46 \end{bmatrix}$ (4×3)

    $F.G\ (4 \times 3)(3 \times 3) = \begin{bmatrix} 10 & 1 & 18 \\ 12 & -3 & 30 \\ 16 & -5 & 30 \\ 18 & -1 & 38 \end{bmatrix}$ (4×3)

    $C.D\ (2 \times 4)(4 \times 2) = \begin{bmatrix} 25 & 30 \\ 112 & 43 \end{bmatrix}$ (2×2)

    $A.E\ (2 \times 4)(4 \times 4) = \begin{bmatrix} 22 & 12 & 5 & 28 \\ 16 & 26 & 5 & 35 \end{bmatrix}$ (2×4)

4 $\begin{aligned} x' &= x+3 \\ y' &= y+4 \end{aligned}$ Translation 4 units upwards and 3 units horizontally.

5 $\begin{aligned} x' &= x+3 \\ y' &= -y-4 \end{aligned}$ Translation as in question 4 followed by a reflection in the x-axis.

Examples XXIV

1 $4x^2 + 6xy + 2y^2$

2 $x^2 + 4xy + y^2$

3 $[x \quad y]\begin{bmatrix} 1 & 1 \\ 1 & 1 \end{bmatrix}\begin{bmatrix} x \\ y \end{bmatrix}$

4 $[x \quad y]\begin{bmatrix} 2 & 3 \\ 3 & 6 \end{bmatrix}\begin{bmatrix} x \\ y \end{bmatrix}$

5 $[x \quad y]\begin{bmatrix} 2 & \frac{3}{2} \\ \frac{3}{2} & 6 \end{bmatrix}\begin{bmatrix} x \\ y \end{bmatrix}$

6 $[x \quad y]\begin{bmatrix} x \\ y \end{bmatrix}$

7 $[x \quad y]\begin{bmatrix} x \\ y \end{bmatrix} = 25$

8 $2x^2 + 5y^2$

9 $x = -3$ or $-\frac{1}{2}$

10 $x^2 + y^2 + 6x + 4y - 3 = 0$

11 $[x \quad y \quad 1]\begin{bmatrix} 1 & 0 & 3 \\ 0 & 1 & -2 \\ 3 & -2 & 9 \end{bmatrix}\begin{bmatrix} x \\ y \\ 1 \end{bmatrix} = 0$

12 $[x \quad y \quad 1]\begin{bmatrix} 1 & 0 & 3 \\ 0 & 1 & -2 \\ 3 & -2 & 9 \end{bmatrix}\begin{bmatrix} x' \\ y' \\ 1 \end{bmatrix} = 0$.

13 $x^2 + y^2 + 9x + 6y + 3xz + 2yz - 3z^2 = 0$

Examples XXV

1 $A^t = \begin{bmatrix} 2 & 4 \\ 3 & 7 \end{bmatrix}$. $B^t = \begin{bmatrix} -2 & -3 \\ 2 & 2 \end{bmatrix}$

$(AB)^t = \begin{bmatrix} -13 & -29 \\ 10 & 22 \end{bmatrix}$ $B^t A^t = \begin{bmatrix} -13 & -29 \\ 10 & 22 \end{bmatrix}$

2 $C^t = \begin{bmatrix} 2 & 3 \\ -1 & 4 \end{bmatrix}$ $(ABC)^t = \begin{bmatrix} 4 & 8 \\ 53 & 117 \end{bmatrix}$

$$C^t(AB)^t = \begin{bmatrix} 4 & 8 \\ 53 & 117 \end{bmatrix} \qquad C^t B^t A^t = \begin{bmatrix} 4 & 8 \\ 53 & 117 \end{bmatrix}$$

3 $\quad AB = \begin{bmatrix} -13 & 10 \\ -29 & 22 \end{bmatrix} \qquad (AB)^{-1} = \frac{1}{4}\begin{bmatrix} 22 & -10 \\ 29 & -13 \end{bmatrix}$

$$B^{-1}A^{-1} = \frac{1}{4}\begin{bmatrix} 22 & -10 \\ 29 & -13 \end{bmatrix}$$

4 $\quad (C^{-1}) = \frac{1}{11}\begin{bmatrix} 4 & -3 \\ 1 & 2 \end{bmatrix} \qquad (C^t)^{-1} = \frac{1}{11}\begin{bmatrix} 4 & -3 \\ 1 & 2 \end{bmatrix}$

5 (a) $\quad P^t = \begin{bmatrix} 1 & 2 & 0 \\ 0 & 1 & 1 \\ 3 & 4 & 3 \end{bmatrix} \qquad Q^t = \begin{bmatrix} 3 & 4 & 1 \\ 2 & 2 & 3 \\ 1 & 2 & 0 \end{bmatrix}$

$$(PQ)^t = \begin{bmatrix} 6 & 14 & 7 \\ 11 & 18 & 11 \\ 1 & 4 & 2 \end{bmatrix} \qquad Q^t P^t = \begin{bmatrix} 6 & 14 & 7 \\ 11 & 18 & 11 \\ 1 & 4 & 2 \end{bmatrix}$$

(b) $\quad P^{-1} = \frac{1}{5}\begin{bmatrix} -1 & 3 & -3 \\ -6 & 3 & 2 \\ 2 & -1 & 1 \end{bmatrix} \qquad Q^{-1} = -\frac{1}{4}\begin{bmatrix} -6 & 3 & 2 \\ 2 & -1 & -2 \\ 10 & -7 & -2 \end{bmatrix}$

$$(PQ)^{-1} = -\frac{1}{20}\begin{bmatrix} -8 & -11 & 26 \\ 0 & 5 & -10 \\ 28 & 11 & -46 \end{bmatrix}$$

$$Q^{-1}P^{-1} = -\frac{1}{20}\begin{bmatrix} -8 & -11 & 26 \\ 0 & 5 & -10 \\ 28 & 11 & -46 \end{bmatrix}$$

7 $\quad (A-B)(A+B) = A^2 + AB - BA - B^2$ and $AB \neq BA$

8 $\quad I - A^2$

Examples XXVI

1 Linearly independent

2 Linearly independent

3 No

4 No. Linearly independent

5 $ad - bc = 0$

6 $p - 2q + r = 0$ $\Delta = 0$ because they are linearly dependent

7 No. Linearly independent

8 Yes

9 $\Delta = 0$ when linear dependence is involved

Examples XXVII

1 2

2 3

3 2

4 1 $|D| = 0$

5 2 $|E| = 0$

6 4

Index